LESSON MASTER 1–1
QUESTIONS ON SPUR OBJECTIVES

■SKILLS   *Objective A (See pages 50–53 for objectives.)*
In 1–4, convert the fractions to decimals and write an inequality to compare them.

1. $\frac{5}{8}$, $\frac{2}{3}$ _____

2. $\frac{5}{12}$, $\frac{7}{16}$ _____

3. $\frac{13}{20}$, $\frac{5}{8}$ _____

4. $\frac{27}{41}$, $\frac{31}{45}$ _____

■SKILLS   *Objective B*
In 5 and 6, use trial and error to find which of the given numbers are solutions to the open sentences.

5. $4x + 3 = 15$ 1, 3, 5 _____

6. $5x + 9 = 7x + 1$ 4, 5, 6 _____

In 7 and 8, find three solutions to each inequality.

7. $4x - 2 > 11$ _____

8. $x + 11 \geq 2x + 7$ _____

■REPRESENTATIONS   *Objective K*
In 9–12, write an inequality to describe each graph. Use the variable that is next to the graph.

9.

_____

10.
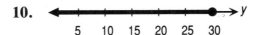

_____

11.

_____

12.

_____

In 13–16, graph the inequality given or suggested by the situation.

13. I weigh between 40 kg and 50 kg.

14. Our teacher is at least 30 years old but younger than 55.

15. $-2 < m$

16. $20 \geq c$

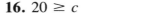

NAME _____

■**USES**   *Objective H* *(See pages 50–53 for objectives.)*
1. a. A sample group of students was asked how much allowance each received during the week. They received $5, $4, $5, $7, $5, $4, $6, $3, $5. Find the mean, median, and mode.

Mean: _____   Median: _____   Mode: _____

b. *True or false* There are as many amounts greater than or equal to the mean as there are less than or equal to the mean.   _____

2. In ten games played, the points scored by the football team were 21, 14, 15, 3, 10, 15, 28, 20, 12, 10. Find the mean, median, and mode.

Mean: _____   Median: _____   Mode: _____

3. *True or false* The mean is always larger than the median.   _____

4. Give a set of data which has two modes.   _____

5. Give a set of data in which the mean and the median are the same.   _____

In 6–8, which measure of central tendency (mean, median, mode) do you think is the best statistic to use to find the answer?

6. Jay did 90, 100, 100, 100, 100, and 100 sit-ups in six workouts. How many sit-ups does Jay usually do in each workout?   _____

7. Caryl received quiz scores of 0, 90, 94, 96, and 100. What is her "average" score?   _____

8. Six students earned $2, $2, $4, $4, $6, and $6 weeding flower beds. What is the "average" payment for this job?   _____

■**REPRESENTATIONS**   *Objective L*
9. Russ worked twelve days at his part-time job in February, with his time card showing the following hours: 1.5, 4, 2.5, 5, 3, 3.5, 2.5, 6, 2.5, 2, 2, and 4.5. Draw a dot frequency diagram for this data.

Algebra © Scott, Foresman and Company

LESSON MASTER 1-2
(page 2)

10. Find the mean, median, and mode for the data given in the previous question.

Mean: _____ Median: _____ Mode: _____

11. Parents of a group of students reported the years of schooling they had (excluding kindergarten). The dot frequency diagram shows their responses.

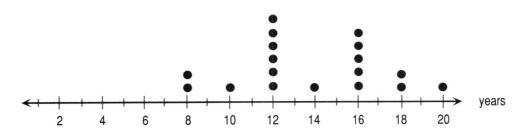

a. Find the mean, median, and mode.

Mean: _____ Median: _____ Mode: _____

b. *True or false* Half of the parents had some schooling beyond high school. _____

12. Below are the state sales tax rates charged on restaurant meals in the 50 states.

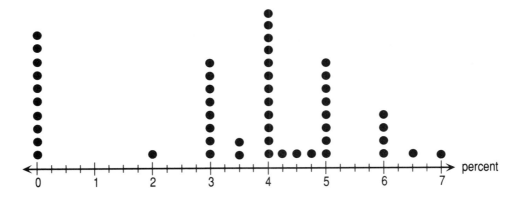

a. How many states charge 4% or less? _____

b. How many states use tax rates that involve a fraction of a percent? _____

c. Find the mode for the data. _____

d. Find the mean for the data. _____

LESSON **MASTER** **1-3**
QUESTIONS ON **SPUR** OBJECTIVES

■**REPRESENTATIONS**   *Objective K (See pages 50–53 for objectives.)*

1. An automobile manufacturer advertises that its car will get from 28 to 35 miles per gallon depending on the speed at which the car is driven.

   a. Express this interval as an inequality using *m* for mileage.

   _____

   b. Graph the inequality.

   ←──────────────────────────────→

2. Graph the closed interval 16 ± 0.5.

   ←──────────────────────────────→

In 3–6, graph the inequality.

3. $2 \le x < 8$

   ←──────────────────→

4. $25 > y > 15$

   ←──────────────────→

5. $\{n \le 5$ where *n* is a whole number$\}$

   ←──────────────────→

6. $\{p < 12$ where *p* is a whole number$\}$

   ←──────────────────→

7. Graph the open interval from 20 to 50.

   ←──────────────────────────────→

8. An interval has a range of 8 and midpoint 5. Graph the interval.

   ←──────────────────────────────→

In 9 and 10, find the range of the interval.

9. 36 ± 8 _____

10. 4 ± 1.2 _____

11. The number of *A*'s given by a group of algebra teachers varied from 2 to 9. Draw a graph showing this interval.

   ←──────────────────────────────→

LESSON MASTER 1–4
QUESTIONS ON SPUR OBJECTIVES

■**SKILLS** *Objective C (See pages 50–53 for objectives.)*
In 1–3, evaluate the numerical expressions.

1. $12 + 2 * 4$ _____

2. $16 - \frac{8}{2} + 6$ _____

3. $\frac{3 + 7}{2} + 3$ _____

4. *True or false* $3x^2 = (3x)^2$ _____

5. Find the value of $3(m + n)$ when $m = 1.2$ and $n = 2.6$ _____

6. Evaluate $\frac{r + s}{r - s}$ when $r = 5$ and $s = 3$. _____

7. Evaluate $9b^2$ when $b = \frac{1}{3}$. _____

8. Evaluate $\left(\frac{3n}{4}\right)^2$ when $n = 2$. _____

■**SKILLS** *Objective D*
9. If the program below is run, and 1.6 is the input, what will be printed?

```
10   PRINT "EVALUATE AN EXPRESSION"
20   PRINT "ENTER A NUMBER"
30   INPUT X
40   PRINT 6 + 32/X − 10
50   END
```

_____

_____

10. The formula for changing Celsius temperature to Fahrenheit is:
$$F = \frac{9}{5}C + 32$$

a. Write a computer program which will find F for an input of any C.

b. What is the Fahrenheit temperature when $C = 28$? _____

Algebra © Scott, Foresman and Company

5

LESSON **MASTER** **1–5**
QUESTIONS ON **SPUR** OBJECTIVES

■**SKILLS**   *Objective D (See pages 50–53 for objectives.)*
1. When the program below is run, what will be printed if 3 is input?

```
10   PRINT "ENTER A NUMBER"
20   INPUT N
30   LET D = (N − 1) * (N + 1) + 2
40   PRINT N, D
50   END
```

■**USES**   *Objective I*
2. In a league with n teams, each team plays every
other team twice (home and away). The total
number of games played is $n(n − 1)$. How
many games are played in an 8-team league?   _____

3. The distance, in feet, required to stop a car
going s miles per hour is about

$$s + \frac{s^2}{20}.$$

How many feet will a car going 60 mph take to
stop?   _____

4. The lateral area (where the label is placed) of a
can of beans is $2\pi rh$, where r is the radius of
the bottom, and h the height of the can. Find the
lateral area if the radius is 5 cm and the height
14 cm.   _____

5. In some schools, the grade point average is
given by:

$$\frac{4a + 3b + 2c + d}{a + b + c + d + f}.$$

where a is the number of A's, b is the number
of B's, c is the number of C's, d is the number
of D's, and f is the number of F's. Carol had
2 A's, 2 B's and a D on her report card. Find
her grade point average.   _____

6. Threshold weight is the maximum weight for a
person in good health. For men aged 40–49, the
threshold weight in pounds is given by

$$\left(\frac{h}{12.3}\right)^3 \qquad h \text{ is height in inches}$$

What is the threshold weight for a 45-year-old
man 67 in. tall?   _____

Algebra © Scott, Foresman and Company

LESSON MASTER 1–6
QUESTIONS ON **SPUR** OBJECTIVES

■**PROPERTIES**   *Objective E (See pages 50–53 for objectives.)*
In 1–3, use the set $\{3, 1.2, -4, 0, \sqrt{3}\}$.

1. Which elements are whole numbers?   _____

2. Which elements are integers?   _____

3. Which elements are real numbers?   _____

In 4–6, let S be the solution set. Find N(S).

4. $4 < x \leq 8$ where the domain is W, the set of
   whole numbers.   _____

5. $n^2 = 4$ where the domain is I.   _____

6. $x + 2 = 5$ where the domain is R.   _____

7. If S = the set of states of the U.S. and R = the set of U.S. Senators,
   compare N(S) and N(R).

   _____

8. *True or false*   The set of living dinosaurs = ∅.   _____

■**USES**   *Objective G*
**In 9–12, a set is given. State whether the set is discrete or continuous and
give a sample element of the set.**

9. the set of tonight's TV programs   _____

10. the set of distances from school   _____

11. the set of all integers   _____

12. the set of fractions between 0 and 1   _____

In 13–15, choose a domain for the variable from these:
real numbers   whole numbers   positive real numbers   integers

13. n, the number of cars in a parking lot.   _____

14. t, the time it takes to walk to school.   _____

15. m, the number of months the rainfall
    in Seattle was greater than 1 inch.   _____

LESSON MASTER 1–7
QUESTIONS ON **SPUR** OBJECTIVES

■**PROPERTIES**   *Objective F (See pages 50–53 for objectives.)*

1. A number is selected randomly from the set of integers between 1 and 50 inclusive. What is the probability that it is divisible by 7?

_____

2. Marie is in a class of 30 students. Five are to be picked at random for a committee. What is the probability that she will be picked?

_____

3. A hexagonal pencil (six faces) has printing on one face. When it is rolled, what is the probability that the printed face will not come up?

_____

4. In a "Pick Three" lottery you pick any three digits. If they come up in the same order as you picked them, you win. If you picked 587, what is the probability you will win?

_____

5. Two fair dice are thrown. Find the probability of each of the following.

a. Sum is 8.

_____

b. Sum is not 2 or 12.

_____

c. Sum is greater than 7.

_____

6. Jack is in a race with three other boys with about his speed. He says, "Either I will win or I won't. So the probability I will win is $\frac{1}{2}$." What is wrong with his argument?

_____

7. A card is picked randomly from a standard deck of 52 playing cards. What is the probability that it is a heart?

_____

8. If an event has the probability of .75 of happening, what is the probability that it won't happen?

_____

9. Which is more likely to happen: throwing a 2 with a die, or throwing a head with a fair coin?

_____

10. A letter is picked at random from the letters in the word *Mississippi*. What is the probability that it is an *s*?

_____

LESSON **MASTER** **1-8**
QUESTIONS ON **SPUR** OBJECTIVES

■**SKILLS**   *Objective A*   *(See pages 50–53 for objectives.)*
In 1–6, simplify using the Equal Fractions Property.

1. $\dfrac{42}{315}$ _____

2. $\dfrac{4a}{9ab}$ _____

3. $\dfrac{4\pi r^2}{2\pi r}$ _____

4. $\dfrac{11abc}{44a}$ _____

5. $\dfrac{2(x + y)}{4(x + y)}$ _____

6. $\dfrac{35rs^3}{21rs^2}$ _____

7. *True or false*   By the Equal Fractions
Property, $\dfrac{x + 3}{x + 6} = \dfrac{1}{2}$.

_____

8. What is x if $\dfrac{3x}{25} = \dfrac{24}{100}$?

_____

■**USES**   *Objective J*

9. In a presidential preference poll, 52% preferred candidate A, 44% preferred
candidate B, and 4% were undecided. Give two possibilities for the number
of people polled, and how many were in each group.

_____

_____

_____

10. In 1982 there were 26 physicians for every 100,000 people in India. If the
population of India was 713 million, about how many physicians were
there in India?

_____

11. A 1982 Nielsen poll showed 50,150,000 American households out of
83,300,000 watched the final episode of M*A*S*H. What was the relative
frequency of a household watching the program?

_____

12. An event occurs n times out of 100 possibilities. What is its relative
frequency?

_____

LESSON MASTER 2–1
QUESTIONS ON SPUR OBJECTIVES

■PROPERTIES *Objective E (See pages 102–105 for objectives.)*
In 1–6, identify what property of addition is given.

1. $3 + -2 = -2 + 3$ _____

2. $(a + 4) + 6 = a + (4 + 6)$ _____

3. $(x + 3) + 2 = 2 + (x + 3)$ _____

4. $4 + (6 + -2) = 4 + (-2 + 6)$ _____

5. $3 + (-2 + a) = (3 + -2) + a$ _____

6. $m + (b + -3) + 3 = m + b + (-3 + 3)$ _____

In 7–10, use the associative and commutative properties to add mentally.

7. $9 + -3 + 2 + -6$ _____

8. $3.2 + -0.6 + -0.2 + 4.6$ _____

9. $998 + 200 + 2 + 50$ _____

10. $\frac{3}{5} + \frac{-1}{3} + \frac{2}{5}$ _____

■USES *Objective H*

11. For the first four months of the year (January–April), the profits of Patty's Pizza Co. were $540, $120, $460, and $180. Mentally find the total for this period.

_____

12. In a game show, Frank won $100 on the first question and n dollars on the second but lost q dollars on the third. He ended up with $300. Write a sentence relating these quantities.

_____

13. Before a summer storm, the temperature was 86°. It then fell $d°$ and later rose 5°. The new temperature was less than 80°. Write a sentence for the final temperature and simplify.

_____

14. Write an expression for the perimeter of this triangle.

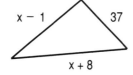

_____

Algebra © Scott, Foresman and Company

LESSON MASTER 2-2
QUESTIONS ON SPUR OBJECTIVES

■SKILLS   *Objective B* *(See pages 102–105 for objectives.)*
In 1–8, simplify.

1. -3 + t + -8

_____

2. $5x$ + -4x + 7x

_____

3. $6a$ + -7b + -3 + -2a

_____

4. 0 + -5a

_____

5. -(-5) + y

_____

6. $7a$ + $6x$ + -7a

_____

7. -12t^2 + 8t + -3t^2

_____

8. 2.3x + 5.1 + -4.6x

_____

■PROPERTIES   *Objective E*
In 9–14, an instance of what property is given?

9. If x = -3, then -x = 3.   _____

10. -ab + 0 = -ab _____

11. $7y$ + -10y = -3y _____

12. If s = -6, then -(s) = 6.   _____

13. xy + -xy = 0   _____

14. Jog 20 meters east, then 20 meters
west, and you are back where you
started.   _____

■USES   *Objective H*

15. A girl lost 10 lb, then gained 3 lb, then lost 4 lb. What is the total change
in her weight?

_____

16. A boy received gifts of g dollars and h dollars and spent x dollars, winding
up with $3.50. Write an equation representing this situation.

_____

LESSON **MASTER** 2-3
QUESTIONS ON **SPUR** OBJECTIVES

■**SKILLS** *Objective A (See pages 102–105 for objectives.)*
In 1–8, write as a single fraction.

1. $\frac{2}{3} + \frac{3}{4}$ _____

2. $\frac{1}{3} + \frac{-1}{6} + \frac{3}{8}$ _____

3. $-2\frac{3}{5} + -3\frac{8}{15}$ _____

4. $\frac{x}{5} + \frac{4}{5}$ _____

5. $\frac{p}{18} + \frac{5}{6}$ _____

6. $\frac{12}{c} + \frac{7}{c}$ _____

7. $\frac{a}{m} + \frac{1}{n}$ _____

8. $\frac{x}{r} + \frac{y}{s}$ _____

9. Juan owned a stock whose value rose $\frac{5}{8}$ point on Monday, rose $\frac{1}{4}$ point on Tuesday, and fell $1\frac{1}{2}$ points on Wednesday. What was the overall change in his stock's value for these three days?

_____

10. What is the perimeter of a rectangle with length $2\frac{1}{10}$ and width $1\frac{3}{5}$?

_____

11. Represent the perimeter of a triangle with sides $1\frac{1}{8}$, $2\frac{4}{5}$, and x as a simplified algebraic expression.

_____

■**PROPERTIES** *Objective E*
In 12–15, identify what property of addition is given.

12. $\frac{5}{12} + 0 = \frac{5}{12}$ _____

13. $3x + 5 + 2x = 5x + 5$ _____

14. $-(-x) = x$ _____

15. $\frac{x}{13} + \frac{-x}{13} = 0$ _____

Algebra © Scott, Foresman and Company

LESSON MASTER 2-4
QUESTIONS ON SPUR OBJECTIVES

■**REPRESENTATIONS** *Objective K (See pages 102–105 for objectives.)*

1. Plot three vertices of a square (1, 3), (1, 6), and (4, 6). Find and plot the fourth vertex. Connect the vertices in order.

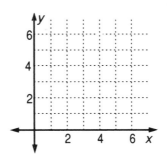

2. a. Toss four coins ten times. Plot the data as ordered pairs which show: (number of the toss, number of heads on the toss).

b. Which number of heads occurred most often?

_____

Least often?

_____

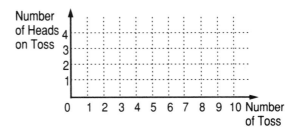

3. a. The following ordered pairs show (year, net cash flow from U.S. Savings Bonds, in billions): (1975, 4), (1977, 4.7), 1979, -0.8), (1981, -4.3). Draw a graph for this data. Label the axes.

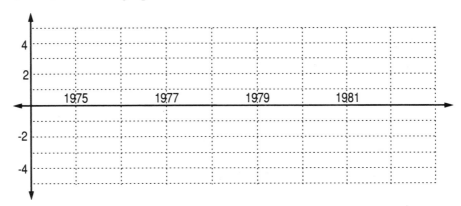

b. During which two-year period was the decrease greatest?

_____

c. What do the negative numbers mean in 1979 and 1981?

_____

_____

LESSON **MASTER** **2–4**
(page 2)

4. a. A football team made the
following gains and losses on
their first four successive plays:
3, 4, -5, and 9. Plot the data
(play number, yards made on
that play).

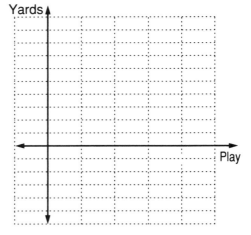

b. Did the team make a first
down? That is, did they gain
more than 10 yards?

_____

5. This graph shows the number of kilowatts of electricity being used by a
family during a day.

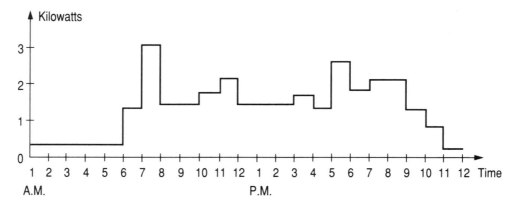

a. What do you think happened at 6 A.M.?

_____

_____

b. How many kilowatts were being used between 7 and 8 A.M.?

_____

c. Why do you think it was so high?

_____

_____

d. At what time do you think the last person went to bed for the night?

_____

14

LESSON MASTER 2-5
QUESTIONS ON **SPUR** OBJECTIVES

■**REPRESENTATIONS**   *Objective L (See pages 102–105 for objectives.)*
In 1–4, find the image of the point after the given slide.

1. (-3, -1); 15 units left and 20 units up.   _____

2. (-6, 14); 4 units left and 9 units down.   _____

3. (7.3, -4.9); 3.5 units right and 4.6 units up.   _____

4. (*x*, *y*); 63 units right and 26 units down.   _____

In 5–7, the image of a point after the indicated slide is given. Find the preimage. (Hint: Work backwards.)

5. (4, -2); 6 units left and 4 units up.   _____

6. (-5, -8); 4 units right and 3 units down.   _____

7. (*x* + 6, *y* + 9); 3 units right and 6 units up.   _____

In 8 and 9, find *a* and *b*.

8. (3 + *a*, 2 + *b*) = (-7, 10)   **9.** (*a* + -4, *b* + -6) = (1, 0)

a = _____ *b* = _____   *a* = _____ *b* = _____

10. Graph the image of the triangle after a slide of 3 units right and 4 units down.

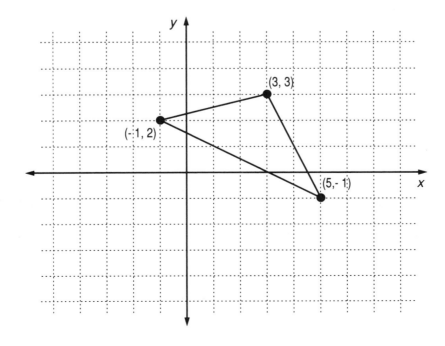

NAME _____

■**SKILLS**   *Objective C (See pages 102–105 for objectives.)*
In 1–4, solve the equations in your head.

1. $x + 5 = 11$ _____

2. $2 + h + 3 = 60$ _____

3. $15 = p + 6$ _____

4. $20 = 5 + x + \text{-}4$ _____

In 5–9, solve and check the equations.

5. $x + \text{-}9 = 11$ _____

6. $\text{-}8 + c + 7 = \text{-}12$ _____

_____

_____

7. $\text{-}12.4 + s = \text{-}14$ _____

8. $p + \text{-}5.7 = \text{-}2.3$ _____

_____

_____

9. $2 = \frac{1}{3} + \frac{t}{6} + \frac{1}{3}$ _____

_____

In 10–13, solve for x.

10. $x + a = c$ _____

11. $x + \text{-}p = r$ _____

12. $k + x = m$ _____

13. $w = x + \text{-}v$ _____

■**PROPERTIES**   *Objective F*
Multiple choice   **In 14 and 15, circle the equation that does not have the same solution as the others.**

14. (a) $4 + x = \text{-}8$ (b) $x + 4 = \text{-}8$ (c) $\text{-}8 + x = 4$ (d) $\text{-}8 = 4 + x$

15. (a) $y + 6 = \text{-}3$ (b) $6 + y = \text{-}3$ (c) $\text{-}3 = 6 + y$ (d) $6 = y + \text{-}3$

■**USES**   *Objective H*
16. The temperature is -10°C. By how much must it
increase to become 4°C?   _____

In 17 and 18, a. write an equation to describe the situation. b. Solve.

17. Peggy opened a savings account with $40. She made a deposit of x dollars,
and withdrew $20. Her balance now is $90.

a. _____   **b.** _____

18. A triangle has sides of 13, 8, and y. The perimeter is 28.

a. _____   **b.** _____

Algebra © Scott, Foresman and Company

NAME _____

■**SKILLS**   *Objective D (See pages 102–105 for objectives.)*
In 1–4, solve.

1. $-13 < d + 5$ _____

2. $11 + w \leq 20$ _____

3. $d + -9.3 \leq -13.7$ _____

4. $\frac{2}{5} + a > \frac{3}{4}$ _____

5. Solve for x: $3a + x < -5a$ _____

6. Solve for y: $y + -8b \geq -12b$ _____

In 7–10, solve in your head.

7. $x + 4 \leq 7$ _____

8. $-3 + y < 6$ _____

9. $2.5 + p > 5.5$ _____

10. $r + \frac{1}{2} \geq \frac{3}{4}$ _____

■**PROPERTIES**   *Objective F*
11. If $s + 13 < -5$, then $s + 13 + -13 < -5 + -13$. This is an instance of what property?

_____

12. Mike adds -8 to both sides of $x + 8 \geq 11$.
What sentence results? _____

13. *Multiple choice*   Circle the inequality that has the same solutions as $-4 < x < 10$.

(a) $10 < x < -4$ (b) $10 \geq x > -4$ (c) $10 > x > -4$ (d) $-4 \leq x \leq 10$

■**USES**   *Objective H*
14. Edna saved \$11 and received \$5 as a gift. If jeans cost at least \$25, how much more does she need? _____

15. The temperature was 10°C. It increased by $n°$. Now it is more than T°C.

a. Give a sentence relating 10, T, and n. _____

b. Solve for n. _____

■**REPRESENTATIONS**   *Objective J*
In 16 and 17, solve and graph the solution set.

16. $y + -1.2 < 5.6$ _____

17. $\frac{1}{2} + a \leq \frac{-3}{2}$ _____

LESSON **MASTER 2-8**
QUESTIONS ON **SPUR** OBJECTIVES

■**PROPERTIES** *Objective G (See pages 102–105 for objectives.)*
In 1–3, find the possible values for n.

1.

2.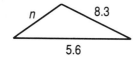

3.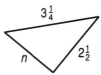

_____   _____   _____

■**USES** *Objective I*
In 4–8, solve using the triangle inequality.

4. It is 160 miles from St. Louis, Missouri, to Bloomington, Illinois. It is 140 miles from Bloomington to Chicago, Illinois. From only this information, what can you say about the distance from St. Louis to Chicago?

_____

5. Richard lives 3.5 km from the library and 1.4 km from school. The distance

of the library from school must be greater than or equal to _____

but less than or equal to _____ .

6. Why is there no triangle with sides of lengths 23 in., 34 in., and 10 in.?

_____

7. Two folding display racks are joined by a hinge as shown.

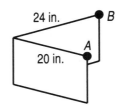

   a. Name three inequalities AB must satisfy.

_____

   b. AB can be no shorter than _____ in.

   c. AB can be no longer than _____ in.

8. A television transmitter is 16 miles from one relay station and 12 miles from another. Describe the possible distances separating the two relay stations.

_____

LESSON **MASTER** **3-1**
QUESTIONS ON **SPUR** OBJECTIVES

■SKILLS *Objective D (See pages 150–152 for objectives.)*
In 1–7, simplify.

1. $11x - 3x + 7x$ _____

2. $-1.8r - .4r + 2.3r$ _____

3. $3d - \dfrac{d}{4} - \dfrac{-5d}{2}$ _____

4. $x^2 - -2x - 3x^2$ _____

5. $4t - (-6t + 4)$ _____

6. $-63 - 44 + 17 - -40 - 6$ _____

7. $-6z^2 - -4z^3 + 8z^3 - 9z^2$ _____

■PROPERTIES *Objective E*
In 8–10, rewrite each subtraction as addition.

8. $4 - 6 - -10$ _____

9. $2a - 3b + c$ _____

10. $-3 - h + 4h - -6$ _____

11. Write a key sequence to compute $-47 - -86$ using the $\boxed{+}$ and $\boxed{+/-}$ keys on your calculator.

_____

12. Evaluate $-f - g$ when $f = -10$ and $g = 12$. _____

13. Evaluate $-(2u - 3v)$ when $u = 4$ and $v = 7$. _____

14. Evaluate $6 - (-x - y)$ when $x = 2$ and $y = -5$. _____

LESSON **MASTER 3-2**
QUESTIONS ON **SPUR** OBJECTIVES

■**USES**   *Objective F (See pages 150–152 for objectives.)*

1. The label on a can of paint says it will cover 550 square feet. Tim has used part of the can to paint a wall of W square feet. How much more area can be covered by what is left in the can?

_____

2. A dealer sells a TV set for S dollars. This price includes overhead expenses E and a profit P. How much did the TV cost the dealer?

_____

3. After cutting 115 square meters of a lawn, Carlos has less than 28 square meters to cut. If the lawn area is M square meters, write an inequality to describe the possible values of M.

_____

4. Last year Mrs. Chen's arithmetic class mean was 7 points below passing on a basic skills test. This year it was 8 points above passing. By how much did it improve this year?

_____

5. In the first football game, the fullback's average gain per carry was -2.3 yards. In the second game it was 3.2 yards. By how much did it increase?

_____

6. The highest temperature ever recorded in Fairbanks, Alaska, is 84°F. The lowest temperature is -40°F. What is the difference between these two temperatures?

_____

7. The closing price for ABC stock was d dollars. If the change for the day was $-3\frac{1}{8}$, what was the opening price?

_____

8. In a presidential poll, $n\%$ favored candidate A, $m\%$ favored candidate B, and the rest had no opinion. What percent had no opinion?

_____

Algebra © Scott, Foresman and Company

LESSON MASTER 3-3
QUESTIONS ON SPUR OBJECTIVES

■SKILLS *Objective B* *(See pages 150–152 for objectives.)*
In 1–4, solve and check.

1. $p - 34 = -8$ _____

2. $4.5 = r - 3.8$ _____

3. $x - 11 > -5$ _____

4. $\frac{5}{8} \geq y - \frac{3}{4}$ _____

In 5–10, solve for x.

5. $x - a = 19$ _____

6. $k = x - 12$ _____

7. $x - p = 3p$ _____

8. $-\frac{3}{4}d = x - \frac{d}{2}$ _____

9. $g < x - 32$ _____

10. $x - c > b$ _____

■SKILLS *Objective D*
In 11–14, simplify.

11. $6h + h - 4h$ _____

12. $4 + (x - 8)$ _____

13. $3x + 5 - 2x$ _____

14. $-9x - x + 10x$ _____

■USES *Objective F*

15. The range of scores on an algebra test was R. The minimum score was 60. Write and solve an equation to find the maximum score h.

_____

16. To lose weight, Sonya had to reduce her daily caloric intake to less than 1800 calories. By eliminating desserts she removed 600 calories and is now losing weight. If her previous intake was c calories, write an inequality describing the situation.

_____

17. Mr. Swenson has saved $1500 for a down payment on an automobile. If the automobile costs T dollars, how much will he have to borrow?

_____

LESSON MASTER 3–4
QUESTIONS ON SPUR OBJECTIVES

■SKILLS   *Objective A (See pages 150–152 for objectives.)*
In 1–6, find the intersection of the sets.

1. $A = \{4, 9, 13, 17\}$, $B = \{1, 9, 15, 17\}$ _____

2. $C = \{1, 3, 5\}$, $D = \{3, 5, 7, 9, 11\}$ _____

3. $F = \{12, 14\}$, $G = \{14, 16\}$, $H = \{14, 15\}$ _____

4. $J = \{20, 30, 40\}$, $K = \{10, 20, 30, 40\}$ _____

5. $L = \{101, 102, 103\}$, $M = \{104, 105, 106\}$ _____

6. $P = \emptyset$, $Q = \{2, 4, 6\}$ _____

■REPRESENTATIONS   *Objective H*
In 7–11, graph the solutions. The domain is the real numbers.

7. $x < 12$ and $x < 7$ ⟵———————————————————⟶

8. $y > -\frac{1}{2}$ and $y \le \frac{1}{2}$ ⟵———————————————————⟶

9. $n \ge 0$ and $n > 3$ ⟵———————————————————⟶

10. $r < 2$ and $r > 5$ ⟵———————————————————⟶

11. $t \le 120$ and $t > 80$ ⟵———————————————————⟶

■REPRESENTATIONS   *Objective I*
In 12 and 13, draw a Venn diagram showing the two sets.

12. $A = \{-3, -1, 0, 5\}$
    $B = \{-8, -1, 0, 7\}$

13. $C = \{1, 2, 3, 4\}$
    $D = \{0, 1, 2, 3, 4, 5\}$

14. Refer to the Venn diagram.
    What can you say about $X \cap Y$?

15. Shade in $Z \cap W$.

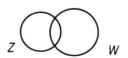

LESSON MASTER 3–5
QUESTIONS ON SPUR OBJECTIVES

■SKILLS   *Objective A (See pages 150–152 for objectives.)*
In 1–6, A = {-1, 1, 7, 12}, B = {-5, 1, 7, 10, 20}, and C = {-3, 1, 7, 10, 30}. Describe:

1. $A \cup B$.

2. $B \cup C$.

3. $A \cup (B \cap C)$.

4. $(A \cup B) \cap C$.

5. $(C \cup A) \cap B$.

6. $(C \cap B) \cup (A \cap B)$.

■REPRESENTATIONS   *Objective H*
In 7–11, graph all solutions on a number line. The domain is the set of real numbers.

7. $x > 2$ or $x \geq 5$

8. $y \leq 3$ or $y > 6$

9. $h > -1$ or $h < 1$

10. $0 \leq t < 3$ or $t > 7$

11. $-2 < z \leq 2$ or $4 \leq z < 6$

■REPRESENTATIONS   *Objective I*
In 12 and 13, A = {-2, 0, 2, 4}, B = {-1, 0, 1, 2}, and C = {0, 1, 2, 3, 4}. Draw and shade a Venn diagram to illustrate each expression.

12. $(A \cup B) \cap C$.

13. $A \cup (B \cap C)$.

LESSON **MASTER** **3-6**
QUESTIONS ON **SPUR** OBJECTIVES

■**USES** *Objective G (See pages 150–152 for objectives.)*
In 1 and 2, find N($A \cup B$) if A and B are mutually exclusive.

1. N(A) = 4, N(B) = 9 _____

2. N(A) = 72, N(B) = 36 _____

In 3 and 4, find N($A \cup B$).

3. N(A) = 32, N(B) = 24, N($A \cap B$) = 8 _____

4. N(A) = 153, N(B) = 147, N($A \cap B$) = 94 _____

5. On the Sluggers baseball squad, a total of 8 players can play infield (includes pitchers and catchers), 7 can play outfield and 3 can play either infield or outfield. How many players are on the squad?

_____

6. There are 28 students in the Drama Club and 32 students in the Chorus. If there are 50 students altogether, how many are in both?

_____

7. In a poll of fast food preferences, 100 liked hamburgers, 75 liked pizza, 50 like chicken, 10 liked hamburgers and pizza only, 10 liked hamburgers and chicken only, 5 liked pizza and chicken only, and 10 liked all three. How many people were polled? Draw a Venn diagram to illustrate the situation.

_____

In 8 and 9, find P($A \cup B$).

8. P(A) = $\frac{1}{2}$, P(B) = $\frac{1}{3}$, P($A \cap B$) = 0 _____

9. P(A) = $\frac{1}{4}$, P(B) = $\frac{4}{9}$, P($A \cap B$) = $\frac{5}{36}$ _____

10. What is the probability of rolling either an even number or a prime number with a single die? _____

11. In a group of 100 car owners, 47 change their own oil, 61 wash their own car, and 38 do both. If someone were chosen at random from this group, what is the probability they either change their oil or wash their own car? _____

LESSON MASTER 3–7
QUESTIONS ON **SPUR** OBJECTIVES

■**REPRESENTATIONS**   *Objective J* *(See pages 150–152 for objectives.)*
In 1–4, graph each equation on the same set of axes. The domain is the set of real numbers.

1. $x + y = -2$ **2.** $x + y = 0$

3. $y = 3 - x$ **4.** $y = 4 - x$

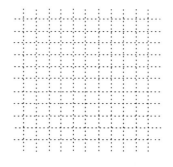

5. Lisa and Terry have a total of 8 albums in their combined collections. Graph all the pairs that show the possible ways the albums may be divided between them.

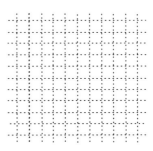

6. A cross-country trucker covered 1000 miles in two days. Graph all possible pairs that show the miles the trucker could have driven on each day.

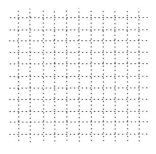

7. Write an equation that describes the points graphed at the right.

_____

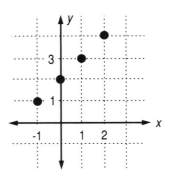

LESSON MASTER 3–8
QUESTIONS ON SPUR OBJECTIVES

■SKILLS *Objective C (See pages 150–152 for objectives.)*
In 1–4, find the measure of a supplement of the given angle.

1. $m\angle A = 43°$ _____

2. $m\angle B = 135°$ _____

3. $m\angle P = c°$ _____

4. $m\angle R = 3x°$ _____

In 5–8, find the measure of a complement of the given angle.

5. $m\angle C = 33°$ _____

6. $m\angle D = 88°$ _____

7. $m\angle S = n°$ _____

8. $m\angle T = 4y°$ _____

9. In the figure find the measures of x, y, and z.

$x =$ _____

$y =$ _____

$z =$ _____

In 10–12, find the unknown measure of the angle of the triangle.

10. _____

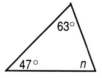

11. _____

12. _____

13. In the figure, find a, x, and y.

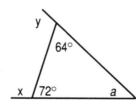

$a =$ _____

$x =$ _____

$y =$ _____

In 14 and 15, find a in each figure.

14. _____

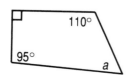

15. _____

Algebra © Scott, Foresman and Company

LESSON **MASTER 4–1**
QUESTIONS ON **SPUR** OBJECTIVES

■**PROPERTIES**   *Objective F (See pages 204–207 for objectives.)*
In 1–4, identify what property of multiplication is given.

1. $a(bc) = (bc)a$ _____

2. $2 \cdot 3h = 6h$ _____

3. $k(x + y) = (x + y)k$

4. $4(25 \cdot 3) = (4 \cdot 25)3$

_____   _____

In 5–8, simplify.

5. $3x \cdot 4y$ _____

6. $am \cdot an$ _____

7. $2ab \cdot 3bc \cdot 4ac$ _____

8. $\frac{1}{2}a \cdot \frac{2}{3}b$ _____

■**USES**   *Objective G*

9. Find the area of a walk 3 ft wide around a
rectangular pool 27 ft by 32 ft. _____

10. Find the area of the shaded part.

11. How many trees are in the orchard
around the barn?

_____   _____

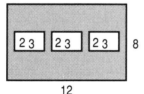

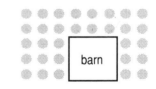

■**USES**   *Objective K*

12. A calculator comes in a box 2 cm × 8 cm ×
10 cm. How many calculators can be shipped in
a box 30 cm × 48 cm × 60 cm? _____

13. A standard room is 10 ft high. What does the
area of the floor have to be for the volume to be
7200 cubic feet? _____

■**REPRESENTATIONS**   *Objective L*
**In 14 and 15, the squares have length 1. What multiplication of fractions
does each drawing represent, and what is the area of the shaded part?**

14.

_____

15.

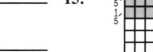

_____

_____

NAME _____

LESSON **MASTER** 4–2
QUESTIONS ON **SPUR** OBJECTIVES

■**SKILLS**   *Objective A* *(See pages 204–207 for objectives.)*
In 1–8, multiply.

1. $\dfrac{5}{8x} \cdot \dfrac{2x}{3}$ _____

2. $\dfrac{4ab}{9} \cdot \dfrac{3}{5a}$ _____

3. $\dfrac{ax}{3} \cdot \dfrac{2}{ay}$ _____

4. $3\frac{1}{3} \cdot 1\frac{1}{5}$ _____

5. $\dfrac{7m}{12} \cdot \dfrac{3n}{4m} \cdot \dfrac{1}{7n}$ _____

6. $42g \cdot \dfrac{3}{7}$ _____

7. $\dfrac{24}{11k} \cdot \dfrac{22r}{9} \cdot \dfrac{3k}{8}$ _____

8. $\dfrac{8p}{15} \cdot 45$ _____

■**USES**   *Objective G*

9. In 1984 in the U.S., there were 22.8 motor vehicle deaths per 100,000 population. How many motor vehicle deaths would you then expect in a U.S. city of 3.5 million people?

_____

10. A baseball player's batting average (hits/times at bat) is .300. At that rate, how many times at bat would the player need to get 120 hits?

_____

11. There are 85 calories in one cooked egg, and 3 eggs in an omelet. How many calories are in 2 omelettes?

_____

12. In 1982, there were 77.2 lb of beef per person consumed in the United States. The average family consisted of 3.1 people. Farmers received 57 cents per lb for beef. On the average, how many cents did the farmers receive from each family's purchase of beef?

_____

■**USES**   *Objective K*

13. Susan has 75 stamps in her collection and adds 7 stamps to her collection every month. In how many months will she have 110 stamps? Write an equation to represent this problem and solve the problem.

_____

_____

28

Algebra © Scott, Foresman and Company

LESSON MASTER 4-3
QUESTIONS ON SPUR OBJECTIVES

■**PROPERTIES**   *Objective F (See pages 204–207 for objectives.)*
In 1–8, simplify and name the multiplication property used.

1. $4 \cdot \dfrac{a}{a}$ _____ ; _____

2. $6x \cdot \dfrac{1}{6x}$ _____ ; _____

3. $-1 \cdot -2y$ _____ ; _____

4. $8(2n - 2n)$ _____ ; _____

5. $(-6)(ab)$ _____ ; _____

6. $\dfrac{4k}{4k}(2c - 1)$ _____ ; _____

7. $(x + y) \cdot \dfrac{1}{(x + y)}$ _____ ; _____

8. $(2t + 1)(3t - 1)(0)$ _____ ; _____

In 9–12, write the reciprocal.

9. -1.5   _____

10. $\dfrac{8}{3}$ _____

11. $\dfrac{5}{2x}$ _____

12. $\dfrac{6}{y - 1}$ _____

In 13–18, for what value of the variable is the reciprocal undefined?

13. $\dfrac{2x}{15}$ _____

14. $\dfrac{n}{-5}$ _____

15. $\dfrac{a - 5}{7}$ _____

16. $\dfrac{c + 4}{9b}$ _____

17. y _____

18. $\dfrac{0}{x}$ _____

LESSON **MASTER** 4–4
QUESTIONS ON **SPUR** OBJECTIVES

■SKILLS *Objective B* (See pages 204–207 for objectives.)
In 1–8, solve and check.

1. $17n = 51$ _____

2. $-13k = 65$ _____

3. $-5s = -1.25$ _____

4. $-8.978 = 1.34t$ _____

5. $\frac{3}{4}x = 27$ _____

6. $-7c = 4\frac{1}{5}$ _____

7. $-\frac{6}{25} = -\frac{4}{5}p$ _____

8. $6y - 8y = 2$ _____

In 9–12, solve for x.

9. $3x = a$ _____ **10.** $-bx = h$ _____

11. $\frac{x}{n} = 12$ _____ **12.** $\frac{a}{b}x = c$ _____

■PROPERTIES *Objective F*
13. What property tells you that $6x = 18.6$ is equivalent to $x = 3.1$?

_____

14. To solve $\frac{a}{b}x = \frac{c}{d}$ for x, multiply both sides by _____ .

■USES *Objective K*
15. A plane flies from St. Louis to Chicago, a
distance of 297 miles, in 45 minutes. Use the
formula $d = rt$ to find its average speed. _____

16. Use the formula $I = prt$ to determine the annual
rate of interest r a bank pays if $120 earns $6 in
one year. _____

Algebra © Scott, Foresman and Company

LESSON **MASTER** 4–5
QUESTIONS ON **SPUR** OBJECTIVES

■SKILLS *Objective B* (See pages 204–207 for objectives.)
In 1–4, solve and check.

1. $2x + 3x - 5x = 7.2$ _____

2. $0 = 9y - 6y - 3y$ _____

3. $3n = 8 - 5 - 3$ _____

4. $(3 - 4)x = 5$ _____

■SKILLS *Objective C*
In 5–10, solve and check.

5. $6 - x = 32$ _____

6. $9.3 = 11.5 - y$ _____

7. $330 - s = 0$ _____

8. $-\frac{2}{7} - a = -\frac{3}{7}$ _____

9. $-18.7 - t = -4.9$ _____

10. $\frac{5}{12} = \frac{3}{4} - k$ _____

In 11–16, solve for x.

11. $a - x = b$ _____   **12.** $-c = -d - x$ _____

13. $\frac{2}{5} - x = \frac{3}{7}$ _____   **14.** $\frac{12}{25} = -\frac{24}{25} - x$ _____

15. $1.1a - x = 3.7a$ _____   **16.** $0 = -t - x$ _____

17. Solve for z: $\frac{1}{2} - z = -\frac{4}{7}$ _____

18. If $50 - t = \frac{17}{3}$, what does t equal? _____

NAME _____

■**SKILLS** *Objective D (See pages 204–207 for objectives.)*
In 1–8, solve and check.

1. $6c \leq 42$ _____

2. $-68 > 17d$ _____

3. $-9k > 108$ _____

4. $5.5x \leq 45.1$ _____

5. $-.36 < .144n$ _____

6. $-.7y \geq -6.3$ _____

7. $\frac{2}{5}a \geq 8$ _____

8. $-\frac{5}{12} < -\frac{3}{8}b$ _____

■**PROPERTIES** *Objective F*

9. If $-x < a$, then x _____ $-a$.

10. What inequality results if both sides
    of $-3z \geq -2$ are multiplied by $-\frac{1}{3}$? _____

■**USES** *Objective K*
11. At least how much must the
    radius of a circle be in order for
    the circumference to be at least 88? _____

12. The class has collected $75.50 for
    a pizza party. A large pizza costs
    $9.95.

    a. Write an inequality to find how
    many pizzas the class can buy. _____

    b. Solve the inequality. _____

13. In 4 minutes, a drain can empty at
    most 40 gallons from a tank.

    a. Write an inequality that tells
    the rate at which the drain
    empties water from the tank. _____

    b. Solve the inequality. _____

32

LESSON **MASTER** 4-7

QUESTIONS ON **SPUR** OBJECTIVES

■**USES** *Objective H (See pages 204–207 for objectives.)*

1. Combination locks have 36 numbers used in three-number combinations. How many different combinations are there? (Assume that the same number cannot be used twice in a row.)

_____

2. A car can be ordered in six different colors, with a choice of two engines and three transmissions. How many different cars can be ordered?

_____

3. On a special sale, pizza can be ordered with two toppings. Suppose there are eight different toppings available.
a. How many pizzas can be ordered with two different toppings?

_____

b. Suppose you can also order "doubles" (pizzas with a double order of the same topping). How many different pizzas can be ordered?

_____

4. A certain state uses three letters followed by three digits for its license plates. The letters I, O, and Q are not used, because they might be read as one or zero. How many licence plates are possible?

_____

5. How many different batting lineups can a 9-member baseball team have if the pitcher must bat last?

_____

6. Suppose a flag is to be made with three stripes of equal areas. Each of the colors red, white, and blue must be used, but can be chosen in any order. If the stripes can be either all vertical or all horizontal, how many different flags can be made?

_____

7. The digits 0, 1, and 8 read the same right side up or upside down.
a. How many different two-digit numbers read the same either way? (A number may not begin with zero.)

_____

b. How many different three-digit numbers can be read the same either way? (A number may not begin with zero.)

_____

Algebra © Scott, Foresman and Company   **33**

LESSON **MASTER** 4–8
QUESTIONS ON **SPUR** OBJECTIVES

■**USES**   *Objective I (See pages 204–207 for objectives.)*
In 1–4, find P(A and B).

1. $P(A) = \frac{3}{5}$, $P(B \text{ given } A) = \frac{5}{8}$ _____

2. $P(B) = .45$, $P(A \text{ given } B) = .30$ _____

3. $P(B) = .6n$, $P(A \text{ given } B) = .4n$ _____

4. $P(A) = \frac{p}{3}$, $P(B \text{ given } A) = \frac{1}{p}$ _____

In 5 and 6, find P(B given A).

5. $P(A \text{ and } B) = \frac{5}{8}$, $P(A) = \frac{3}{4}$ _____

6. $P(A \text{ and } B) = \frac{p}{3}$, $P(A) = \frac{2p}{5}$ _____

In 7 and 8, find P(A).

7. $P(A \text{ and } B) = \frac{1}{12}$, $P(B \text{ given } A) = \frac{2}{3}$ _____

8. $P(A \text{ and } B) = .32r$, $P(B \text{ given } A) = .56r$ _____

9. If two light bulbs in a display are connected in series and one goes out, the other will also go out. The probability that a light bulb will last a month is .95. What is the probability that the display will last a month?

_____

10. In basketball, a one-and-one free throw means that if you make the first one, you get to shoot again. Suppose a player usually makes 75% of his free throws. What is the probability that he will make both shots of a one-and-one free throw?

_____

11. At a carnival booth, you get a prize if you hit a target and knock it off the shelf. The probability that you will hit the target is $\frac{1}{4}$. The probability that it will fall off the shelf if you hit it is $\frac{1}{2}$. What is the probability that you will win a prize?

_____

12. Two letters are picked at random from the letters in the word *mathematics,* without replacement. What is the probability that they are both vowels?

_____

34

LESSON MASTER 4–9
QUESTIONS FOR SPUR OBJECTIVES

■SKILLS   *Objective E (See pages 204–207 for objectives.)*
In 1–6, write as a decimal.

1. $6!$ _____

2. $3! \cdot 2!$ _____

3. $2! + 5!$ _____

4. $7 \cdot 6 \cdot 5!$ _____

5. $\dfrac{5!}{3!2!}$ _____

6. $\dfrac{15!}{13!}$ _____

In 7 and 8, simplify.

7. $\dfrac{(n + 1)!}{n!}$ _____

8. $n \cdot (n - 1)!$ _____

In 9–12, use a calculator to estimate.

9. $16!$ _____

10. $8!7!$ _____

11. $\dfrac{10!}{6!4!}$ _____

12. $\dfrac{9! + 4!}{6!}$ _____

■USES   *Objective J*

13. **a.** Eight gymnasts compete in an event. In how many ways can first and second place be awarded?   _____

    b. In how many different orders can all eight gymnasts finish?   _____

14. **a.** Twelve members of a college basketball squad line up for the national anthem. How many different ways could this be done?   _____

    b. The members select a captain and co-captain from their 12. How many ways can this be done?   _____

15. In how many ways can 6 different books be arranged on a shelf?   _____

16. **a.** How many ways can the letters in the word CATS be arranged?   _____

    b. Write the arrangements that are English words.

    _____

17. Four boys and four girls are to be seated in a row on a stage, alternating boy, girl, boy, girl, etc. How many different seating arrangements are there?

    _____

LESSON **MASTER** 5–1
QUESTIONS ON **SPUR** OBJECTIVES

■SKILLS *Objective A* *(See pages 256–259 for objectives.)*

1. If two numbers have the same sign, what is the sign of the quotient? _____

2. If the result of dividing two numbers is negative, what can you say about the signs of the two numbers? _____

In 3 and 4, rewrite as a multiplication.

3. $\dfrac{x}{y} \div \dfrac{1}{z}$ _____

4. $\dfrac{\ell}{\frac{m}{n}}$ _____

In 5–18, simplify.

5. $\dfrac{3}{5} \div \dfrac{5}{9}$ _____

6. $\dfrac{4a}{15b} \div \dfrac{6a}{25b}$ _____

7. $\dfrac{-7}{12} \div \dfrac{14}{15}$ _____

8. $\dfrac{8}{11} \div \dfrac{-4}{5}$ _____

9. $\dfrac{\frac{3}{16}}{\frac{15}{4}}$ _____

10. $\dfrac{\frac{-2\pi}{9}}{\frac{-4}{3}}$ _____

11. $\dfrac{\frac{18}{1}}{3}$ _____

12. $\dfrac{-28}{\frac{5}{4}}$ _____

13. $\dfrac{35x}{39} \div \dfrac{-42}{65y}$ _____

14. $\dfrac{\frac{-24n}{25p}}{\frac{-6}{5r}}$ _____

15. $\dfrac{\frac{3}{a}}{-20}$ _____

16. $\dfrac{\frac{t}{5}}{6}$ _____

17. $\dfrac{\frac{-15w}{38x}}{\frac{45z}{57y}}$ _____

18. $\dfrac{\frac{-9f}{56g}}{\frac{-15h}{49k}}$ _____

LESSON MASTER 5-2
QUESTIONS ON SPUR OBJECTIVES

■PROPERTIES *Objective D (See pages 256–259 for objectives.)*
In 1–6, what value(s) can the variable not have?

1. $\dfrac{2}{x}$ _____

2. $\dfrac{a}{a - 4}$ _____

3. $\dfrac{b - 3}{b + 5}$ _____

4. $\dfrac{n + 9}{n - 11}$ _____

5. $\dfrac{1.5k}{k - 1.5}$ _____

6. $\dfrac{c - 6.1}{8.3 + c}$ _____

■USES *Objective F*

7. Andre Dawson of the Chicago Cubs earned
$1,850,000 in 1988. If he played in all 162
games, how much was his salary per game? _____

8. There are 30 slices in a certain loaf of bread and
2400 calories per loaf. How many calories
are in each slice? _____

9. Bobby ran $\frac{3}{10}$ of a mile in $1\frac{1}{2}$ minutes. How
many minutes per mile is this? _____

10. In a recent year, there were 46,000 deaths from
motor vehicle accidents in the U.S. If the
population was approximately 226.5 million,
what was the death rate per 100,000 population
due to motor vehicle accidents? _____

■REPRESENTATIONS *Objective L*
11. For the program, what will be printed if the input is

a. 6? _____   **b.** -4? _____

```
10   PRINT "EVALUATE AN EXPRESSION."
20   PRINT "ENTER A VALUE OF A."
30   INPUT A
40   IF A = 6 THEN PRINT "IMPOSSIBLE"
50   IF A <> 6 THEN PRINT (A+2)/(A−6)
60   END
```

12. Write a program to evaluate $(n + 4)/(n + 9)$ for any value of n that is
entered. If the input makes the expression meaningless, the computer
should print "IMPOSSIBLE."

NAME _____

■**USES** *Objective G* *(See pages 256–259 for objectives.)*
1. In a recent year, there were 11,068 births and 9,928 deaths in Alaska. Write the ratio of births to deaths.

_____

2. Jack gets an allowance of $7.50 a week and spends $3.50 a week for lunches. What percent of his allowance is spent for lunch?

_____

3. In the 1980 presidential election there were 35.5 million votes cast for the Democratic candidate and 43.9 million votes for the Republican. What was the ratio of Republican to Democratic votes?

_____

4. *Multiple choice* The rectangle that is considered to be most pleasing to the eye has a length to width ratio of about 1.618. Which rectangle has dimensions which are closest to this ratio?

    (a) 6 cm by 9 cm   (b) 8.5 in. by 11 in.

    (c) 3 in. by 5 in.   (d) 4 ft by 8 ft   _____

5. A pair of jeans which usually sells for $24 is on sale for $6 less. What is the percent of discount?   _____

6. What is the percent of discount of a $119.95 suit which is selling for $99?   _____

7. What is the sales tax rate if you pay 60¢ on a $12.00 item?   _____

8. What is the sales tax rate for a tax of t dollars on an item costing c dollars?   _____

9. A school swim team won 6 out of 8 swimming meets. What is the team's winning percentage?   _____

10. Mr. Gaston bought a stock for d dollars, and sold it for $d + p$ dollars. What was the ratio of his profit to his purchase price?   _____

38

LESSON MASTER 5–4
QUESTIONS ON SPUR OBJECTIVES

■SKILLS   *Objective B* (See pages 256–259 for objectives.)

1. What is 60% of 25?

_____

2. 16 is what percent of 40?

_____

3. 38 is what percent of 20?

_____

4. 65% of what number is 195?

_____

5. What is 140% of 72?

_____

6. 4.5% of what number is .09?

_____

7. 4.62 is what percent of 1.76?

_____

8. What is 0.5% of 40?

_____

■USES   *Objective H*

9. A dealer wants to raise the price of a car by 6.5%. How much should the dealer add to the price of a $7800 car?

_____

10. The population of Omaha, Nebraska went from 346,929 in 1970 to 313,939 in 1980. The 1980 population was what percent of the 1970 population?

_____

11. The United States has about 134 million metric tons of copper deposits. This represents about 18.5% of the world deposits. How many million metric tons of copper deposits does the world have?

_____

12. Sara withdrew $50 from her savings account of $168. About what percent did she withdraw?

_____

13. In the first 50 years of the all-star baseball games, 53 games were played between the National and American Leagues. The National League won 34 of them. What percent did the American League win?

_____

LESSON **MASTER** **5–5**
QUESTIONS ON **SPUR** OBJECTIVES

■**REPRESENTATIONS**   *Objective J (See pages 256–259 for objectives.)*

1. Two squares are drawn inside the rectangle. If a point is selected at random, what is the probability that it lies in the shaded region?

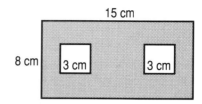

_____

2. A 20-minute audio tape has four songs with times in minutes and seconds as follows: A, 4:30; B, 4:00; C, 5:30; D, 6:00. If the tape is started at any random position, what is the probability that it will be playing song A or C?

_____

3. The total area of the United States is 3,623,420 square miles. This includes 79,537 square miles of water. What is the probability that a satellite which falls at a random location in the U.S. will land in water?

_____

4. In the spinner, any position is equally likely. What is the probability that the spinner lands in region A or C?

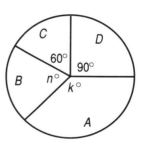

_____

5. A dart lands randomly on the crossword puzzle board. What is the probability that it will land in an unshaded square?

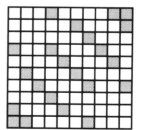

_____

6. The baseball foul lines form an angle of 90°. Suppose that a batter hits a ball with no control over its direction. What is the probability that the ball will go outside the foul lines?

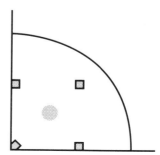

_____

Algebra © Scott, Foresman and Company

LESSON **MASTER** **5–6**
QUESTIONS ON **SPUR** OBJECTIVES

■USES   *Objective H*   *(See pages 256–259 for objectives.)*
1. Helene received a Christmas bonus of 1.5 times her weekly salary. If her weekly salary was *W* dollars, how much was her bonus?

_____

2. After a period of growth, a crystal was 1.2 times its original length. If its new length was 6.4 mm long, what was the original length of the crystal?

_____

3. A blade of grass appears to be 2″ thick under a 250-power microscope. What is its actual thickness?

_____

■REPRESENTATIONS   *Objective M*
In 4 and 5, give the image of point *P* under a size change of magnitude 3.

4. *P*(2, 4) _____   **5.** *P*(-5, -8) _____

In 6 and 7, give the image of point *P* under a size change of magnitude -$\frac{1}{2}$.

6. *P*(-4, 1) _____   **7.** *P*(*x*, -*y*) _____

8. Graph the image of the triangle *ABC* under a size change of magnitude 2.

9. Graph the image of the triangle *PQR* under a size change of -$\frac{2}{3}$.

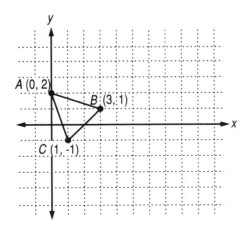

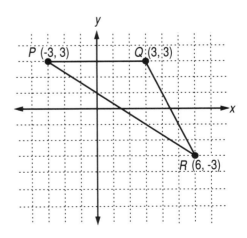

NAME _____

■**SKILLS** *Objective C* *(See pages 256–259 for objectives.)*
In 1–8, solve.

1. $\dfrac{x}{40} = \dfrac{7}{8}$ _____

2. $\dfrac{-3}{5} = \dfrac{9}{y}$ _____

3. $\dfrac{7}{n} = 2.8$ _____

4. $\dfrac{3p}{-16} = \dfrac{21}{4}$ _____

5. $\dfrac{4k}{5} = -18$ _____

6. $\dfrac{1.8}{t} = \dfrac{4.2}{0.5}$ _____

7. $\dfrac{a}{\frac{1}{2}} = \dfrac{4}{\frac{1}{3}}$ _____

8. $\dfrac{-3.5}{0.4t} = \dfrac{-0.5}{6.6}$ _____

■**PROPERTIES** *Objective E*

9. If $\dfrac{p}{r} = \dfrac{2q}{3s}$, then by the Means-Extremes Property _____ = _____ .

10. If $\dfrac{3x}{5} = \dfrac{-2y}{7}$, then $\dfrac{7}{-2y} =$ _____ .

■**USES** *Objective I*

11. Mr. Swenson can plow 3.5 acres in 1.5 hours. At that rate, how long would it take him to plow 10.5 acres?

_____

12. A certain recipe to serve 4 people calls for 280 grams of flour. How many grams of flour are needed if 7 people are to be served the same size portion?

_____

13. Anne earns $48 for each 100 envelopes she addresses. At that rate, how many envelopes will she have to address to earn $200?

_____

14. Ben used 8 gallons of gas to go 230 miles. Under the same driving conditions, how many gallons will he need to go 310 miles?

_____

15. Jon used 2.5 gallons of paint to cover 900 square feet. How many gallons will he need to cover 1300 square feet?

_____

Algebra © Scott, Foresman and Company

LESSON MASTER 5–8
QUESTIONS ON SPUR OBJECTIVES

■**PROPERTIES**   *Objective E* *(See pages 256–259 for objectives.)*

In 1–3, x and y are corresponding sides of similar figures. So are a and b.

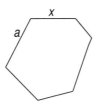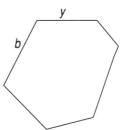

1. If $x = 4$, $y = 9$, and $a = 12$, then $b = $ __?__ .   _____

2. If $x = 1.8$, $a = 0.6$, and $b = 1.1$, then $y = $ __?__ .   _____

3. If $x = \frac{2}{3}$, $y = \frac{1}{2}$, and $b = \frac{3}{5}$, then $a = $ __?__ .   _____

4. What property must be used to answer 1–3?

■**REPRESENTATIONS**   *Objective K*

In 5–7, refer to the similar triangles. Corresponding sides are drawn with the same thickness.

5. Give one ratio of similitude.

_____

6. Find x.   **7.** Find y.

_____   _____

8. A surveyor made the measurements in the diagram to find the length of a pond. $\overline{PQ}$ is parallel to $\overline{RS}$. Find RS.

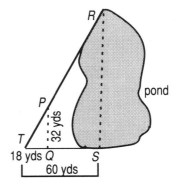

_____

9. A building casts a shadow 51 feet long. At the same time, an 8-foot fence post casts a shadow 6 feet long. How high is the building?

_____

LESSON MASTER 6-1
QUESTIONS ON SPUR OBJECTIVES

■SKILLS *Objective B (See pages 308–311 for objectives.)*
In 1 and 2, solve and check.

1. $4y + 9 = -43$ _____

2. $62 = 5n - 13$ _____

In 3–10, solve.

3. $13a - 72 = 58$ **4.** $6k + 23 = 17$ **5.** $3 + 2v = 17$

_____   _____   _____

6. $28 = 11w - 5$ **7.** $-8 = -8 + 4c$ **8.** $-2 = 13 + 3b$

_____   _____   _____

9. $6p - 16 = 23$ **10.** $-34 = 5t - 18$

_____   _____

■PROPERTIES *Objective D*
In 11–13, identify the property applied.

11. If $3x + 5 = 11$, then $3x = 6$.   _____

12. If $2y + 18 = 12$ then $y + 9 = 6$.   _____

13. If $3t + 1 = 0$, then $6t + 2 = 0$.   _____

■REPRESENTATIONS *Objective J*
14. In the picture, the boxes
are of equal weight and each
cylinder weighs 1 kg.

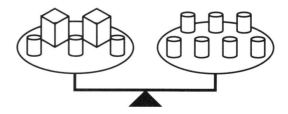

a. Write an equation
representing this
situation.

_____

b. What is the weight of one box? _____

LESSON **MASTER** 6–2
QUESTIONS ON **SPUR** OBJECTIVES

■**SKILLS**   *Objective B (See pages 308–311 for objectives.)*
In 1–8, solve.

1. $2s + 1.5 = 5.5$ **2.** $11.7 + 5.6k = 25.7$ **3.** $-0.7 = 0.8 + .3x$

_____ _____ _____

4. $\frac{5v}{12} - \frac{2}{3} = \frac{1}{6}$ **5.** $5 + 7y - 3 = 37$ **6.** $\frac{3}{4} = \frac{5}{8} + 2a$

_____ _____ _____

7. $65 - 8x = 21$ **8.** $\frac{7}{10} = 1 - \frac{3x}{5}$

_____ _____

■**USES**   *Objective H*

9. Freddie now weighs 260 pounds. To weigh 190 pounds in a half year (26 weeks), how much weight must he lose per week?

_____

10. At the U-Pick Strawberry Farm, Susan paid a total of $5.59 for the following: $.55 for an empty basket and $.48 a pound for the strawberries she picked. How many pounds of strawberries did she pick?

_____

11. Ms. Gower sells stereos. She gets a salary of $250 a week and a 5% commission on her total sales. If she earned a total of $400 one week, what was the total of her sales?

_____

12. As air rises, it cools by expansion according to the formula $T = t - \frac{H}{100}$, where t is the Celsius temperature at the earth's surface, and T is the Celsius temperature at altitude H. If the air temperature at the surface is 25°C, how high must the balloon go to reach a height where the temperature is -5°?

_____

Algebra © Scott, Foresman and Company

LESSON **MASTER** 6-3
QUESTIONS ON **SPUR** OBJECTIVES

■SKILLS *Objective A (See pages 308–311 for objectives.)*
In 1–4, simplify.

1. $2x + x - 0.5x$ _____

2. $n - 0.25n$ _____

3. $n + 0.06n + 10$ _____

4. $6y + 4z - 3y$ _____

■PROPERTIES *Objectives D*
In 5 and 6, simplify using the Distributive Property.

5. $7(2a + 5)$ _____

6. $x + x + 0.5x$ _____

■PROPERTIES *Objective E*
In 7–10, show how the Distributive Property can be used to perform the calculations mentally.

7. $4 \cdot \$9.95$ _____

8. $8 \cdot \$6.03$ _____

9. $202 \cdot 45$ _____

■USES *Objective F*
In 10–13, write and solve an equation for each question.

10. The Grossman's total dinner bill at a restaurant was $17.94. It included a 15% tip. What was the cost of the dinner before the tip?

_____

11. At some hotels, senior citizens get a 20% discount on a room. If the discounted price is $48 for a room, what is the regular price?

_____

■USES *Objective I*

12. Two angles are complementary. One is 4 times as large as the other. What are their measures?

_____

13. Peter opened a savings account that earns 6% in interest a year. He does not withdraw his money, and after a year, he has $402.80 in the account. Find the amount of his initial deposit.

_____

NAME _____

■**USES** *Objective G (See pages 308–311 for objectives.)*
In 1–4, find the difference between two successive terms. Then give a formula for the nth term.

	Difference	*n*th term
1. 2, 5, 8, 11, . . .	_____	_____
2. 15, 11, 7, 3, . . .	_____	_____
3. -1.3, -1.1, -0.9, . . .	_____	_____
4. $\frac{1}{4}, \frac{1}{2}, \frac{3}{4}, 1, . . .$	_____	_____

5. In the sequence 3, 8, 13, 18, . . . , which term is 48? _____

6. In the sequence 14.8, 14.5, 14.2, 13.9, . . . , which term is 11.8? _____

7. In May, a store begins a closeout sale on coats by charging $34 per coat. The store reduces this price $5 per week until no coats remain. After how many weeks will remaining coats sell for $9 each?

_____

8. A taxi company charges $1.10 for the first 0.1 mile, and $.10 for each additional 0.1 mile. If a trip costs a total of $2.60, how many miles is the trip?

_____

9. At 4 P.M. Jill must still drive 286 miles to reach her destination. She would like to stop for the night at 7 P.M. How fast must she drive to be 100 miles from her destination when she stops?

_____

10. In a certain bank, the minimum balance you must have in a checking account to avoid paying a service charge is $100. Ruth has a balance of $638. If she withdraws $48 a month for a car payment and makes no deposits, how many payments can she make without having a service charge?

_____

LESSON **MASTER** **6–5**
QUESTIONS ON **SPUR** OBJECTIVES

■SKILLS   *Objective B (See pages 308–311 for objectives.)*
In 1–8, solve.

1. $3a + 20 = -31$ _____

2. $-c + 4 = -24$ _____

3. $-72 - 18k = 18$ _____

4. $-1.3 - -1.1x = -0.9$ _____

5. $\frac{1}{4}y + -\frac{1}{2} = \frac{3}{4}$ _____

6. $15d + 3d - 26d = -64$ _____

7. $.8m - 4.3m + 3.7m = -8.0$ _____

8. $\frac{1}{2}n + -\frac{5}{4}n = \frac{1}{4}n + \frac{7}{8}$ _____

9. The formula for finding the area of a triangle is $A = \frac{1}{2}bh$, where A is the area, b is the base, and h is the height. What is the height of a triangle that has a base of 3 cm and an area of 12 cm^2?

_____

10. In the sequence 3, 10, 17, 24, . . . , which term of the sequence is 52?

_____

11. Not including the 7% sales tax, a sweater cost $28.42. How much did the sweater cost with tax?

_____

12. The Dennisons went to a Mexican restaurant and ordered tacos. Mr. Dennison ate twice as many tacos as Mrs. Dennison, and Greg Dennison ate three times as many tacos as his mother. If they ordered 12 tacos, how many did Greg eat?

_____

13. A gallon of gasoline costs $1.02 at Bob's filling station. If you pay $11.67 to fill your tank completely, how many gallons of gasoline did you buy? Round to the nearest hundredth.

_____

Algebra © Scott, Foresman and Company

LESSON MASTER 6–6
QUESTIONS ON SPUR OBJECTIVES

■SKILLS   *Objective B* *(See pages 308–311 for objectives.)*
In 1–12, solve.

1. $n + 2 = 3n - 8$

2. $6r - 7 = 3r - 22$

_____

_____

3. $22 - 5a = 47 - 3a$

4. $168 - 11t = 293 - 36t$

_____

_____

5. $1.9 + 1.8x = 8.2x - 6.9$

6. $.072v + .063 = .104v - .093$

_____

_____

7. $\dfrac{2h}{3} + \dfrac{1}{2} = \dfrac{5h}{6} - \dfrac{3}{4}$

8. $\dfrac{9b}{5} - 3 = \dfrac{3b}{10} + 9$

_____

_____

9. $\dfrac{p + 3}{4} = \dfrac{p - 1}{6}$

10. $\dfrac{y - 8}{2} = \dfrac{y + 10}{5}$

_____

_____

11. $2x + 7 - 3x = 4x + 9 - 3x$

12. $16 - 3x - 9 = 28 - 2x + 4$

_____

_____

■PROPERTIES   *Objective D*
In 13 and 14, identify the property being applied.

13. If $\dfrac{2}{A - 3} = \dfrac{3}{A + 1}$,
   then $2A + 2 = 3A - 9$. _____

14. If $3x + a = -2x + 4a$,
   then $5x = 3a$. _____

NAME _____

LESSON **MASTER** **6-6**
(page 2)

■USES *Objective G*

15. A magician says, "I am thinking of a number. Twenty-one less than three times the number is five more than the number." Find the number.

_____

16. A tank that contains 340 gallons of brine is being drained at a rate of 15 gallons per hour. Another tank which starts with 60 gallons is being filled at a rate of 20 gallons per hour. After how many hours will they both hold the same amount?

_____

■USES *Objective I*

17. Janet has $105.00 and spends $5.00 every week. Marlene has $45.00 and saves $10.00 every week. In how many weeks will they have the same amount of money? **a.** Write an equation that describes this situation, and **b.** solve the problem.

a. _____

b. _____

■REPRESENTATIONS *Objective J*

In 18–20, the boxes in each picture are of equal weight. Every cylinder weighs one pound. For each question, a. write an equation in which *B* represents the weight of one box, and b. find the weight of one box.

18. a. _____

b. _____

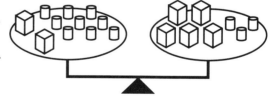

19. a. _____

b. _____

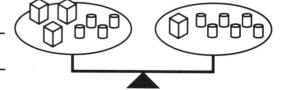

20. a. _____

b. _____

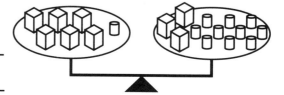

50

LESSON MASTER 6–7
QUESTIONS ON **SPUR** OBJECTIVES

■SKILLS *Objective C (See pages 308–311 for objectives.)*
In 1 and 2, solve and check.

1. $3a + 8 > 14$

2. $19 > 7c - 2$

_____ _____

In 3 and 4, solve and graph the solution on a number line.

3. $11 + 5n < -9$ _____

←————————————→

4. $23 \geq 17 + 6r$ _____

←————————————→

In 5–10, solve.

5. $19 - 4t > 3$

6. $1.4 + 0.6y \leq 5.6$

7. $\frac{2x}{3} - \frac{1}{2} > \frac{1}{3}$

_____ _____ _____

8. $8u + 3 < 13u - 12$

9. $6 \geq 9h - 15 - 2h$

10. $5p + 3 - 2p \leq p$

_____ _____ _____

■PROPERTIES *Objective D*
In 11 and 12, identify the property being used.

11. If $2x + 7 > x - 4$, then $x > -11$.

_____

12. If $-4x - 11 < 12$, then $4x + 11 > -12$.

_____

In 13 and 14, perform the indicated operation on both sides of the inequality.

13. $14a - 3 > 11 - 2a$; add $2a + 3$ to both sides.

_____

14. $31 - c < -4$; multiply both sides by -1.

_____

LESSON **MASTER** **6–8**
QUESTIONS ON **SPUR** OBJECTIVES

■SKILLS *Objective A (See pages 308–311 for objectives.)*
In 1–8, use the Distributive Property to eliminate the parentheses.

1. $2(3a + 2b)$ _____

2. $4(3x - 5)$ _____

3. $0.06(20r + 50s)$ _____

4. $1.12(7p - 4f)$ _____

5. $\frac{2}{3}(9n - 6m)$ _____

6. $\frac{5}{8}(12k + 16t)$ _____

7. $4a(a + 23b + 17c)$ _____

8. $15uv(3v + 2y - 3)$ _____

In 9–12, simplify.

9. $4x + 3y + 2(x - 7y)$ **10.** $9(a + 2b) - 3(2a - 5b)$

11. $4f(6h - 2p + 1) + 2h(5f - 1)$

12. $3(x + 2) + 8(6 - 2x - 3) - 9(5x + 9)$

■SKILLS *Objective B*
In 13–20, solve.

13. $3(2a - 5) = 15$ **14.** $2(c + 7 + 3(c - 4)) = -3$

15. $4(y - 2) - 3(y + 7) = -34$ **16.** $5(2x - 1) = 3(x + 3)$

52 *Continued*   *Algebra* © Scott, Foresman and Company

LESSON MASTER 6-8
(page 2)

17. $\frac{1}{2}(6k + 3) = 4\frac{1}{2}$

18. $\frac{2}{3}(n + 10) = \frac{3}{4}(n + 9)$

_____   _____

19. $0.04(p + 1.1) = 0$

20. $0.8(2p - 3) = 0.6(p - 4)$

_____   _____

■PROPERTIES *Objective D*
In 21–23, identify the property being applied.

21. If $2x + 7y = -5x - y$,
then $7x = -8y$. _____

22. $\frac{1}{2}(3 - 7x) = \frac{3}{2} - \frac{7x}{2}$ _____

23. If $3x = -8a$,
then $x = \frac{-8a}{3}$. _____

■REPRESENTATIONS *Objective J*
In 24–26, write two different expressions that describe the total area of the two rectangles.

24. _____

_____

0.2 cm [ ] 0.2 cm [ ]
0.8 cm   0.6 cm

25. _____

_____

16 in.
a in. [ ]

b in. [ ]

26. _____

_____

3 ft
3 ft [ ]   [ ] y ft
x ft

LESSON MASTER 6–9
QUESTIONS ON SPUR OBJECTIVES

■SKILLS *Objective A (See pages 308–311 for objectives.)*
In 1–8, simplify.

1. $-(2x - 9)$

2. $-(3a - 2b + 6c)$

3. $2 - (w + 4)$

4. $-(2a - 3) + (3a - 6)$

5. $-3(4r + 3s) - (8r + s)$

6. $2.1d + 3.7 - (4.2d - 6.1)$

7. $\dfrac{5m}{12} - \left(\dfrac{7m}{9} + 1\right)$

8. $\dfrac{8k}{15} + \dfrac{7j}{30} - \left(\dfrac{7k}{15} + \dfrac{11j}{30}\right)$

■SKILLS *Objective B*
In 9–12, solve.

9. $(8x - 3) - (5x + 6) = 6$

10. $-(11x - 14) = -8$

11. $2.6 = 1.8 - (0.2x - 1)$

12. $7x - (2x + 1) = 7 - (x - 4)$

■PROPERTIES *Objective D*
In 13 and 14, identify the property being applied.

13. If $12x + -4y = -15x - 3y$,
then $27x = y$. _____

14. $-2(3 - 7x) = -6 + 14x$, _____

LESSON **MASTER** **7–1**
QUESTIONS ON **SPUR** OBJECTIVES

■REPRESENTATIONS   *Objective H (See pages 360–363 for objectives.)*
**In 1 and 2, a. make a table of values, b. graph the line, and
c. answer the question.**

1. $y = 3x - 1$

a.

x	y

b.

c. For what value of y will $(-2, y)$ be on the line?

2. $y = 2 - x$

a.

x	y

b.

c. For what value of x will $(x, 4)$ be on the line?

3. Complete the chart for the graph.

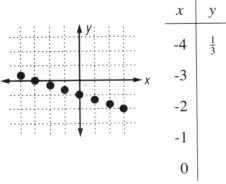

x	y
-4	$\frac{1}{3}$
-3	
-2	
-1	
0	

4. *Multiple choice*   Which equation describes the ordered pairs in the table below?

x	y
0	-8
1	-6
2	-4

(a) $y = x - 8$

(b) $y = 2x - 8$

(c) $y = -2x - 8$

(d) $y = 8 - 2x$

5. The difference d in dollars between the original price p of an item and its sale price of 14 dollars is given by $d = p - 14$. Complete the chart; then graph this relationship.

p	d

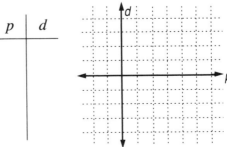

LESSON MASTER 7–2
QUESTIONS ON **SPUR** OBJECTIVES

■**REPRESENTATIONS**   *Objective I (See pages 360–363 for objectives.)*
In 1–4, tell whether the statement is true or false.

1. The graph of $y = 6.1$ is a vertical line.

_____

2. The graph of $x = 6$ is a horizontal line.

_____

3. The boundary of the half plane satisfying $y > 4$ is a dotted line.

_____

4. The boundary of the half plane satisfying $x \le -3.5$ is a solid line.

_____

5. Graph the points in the plane satisfying $x > -1$.

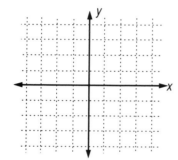

6. Graph the points in the plane satisfying $y \le 2.5$.

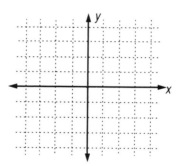

In 7 and 8, give a sentence describing the shaded region.

7. _____

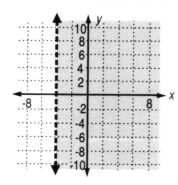

8. _____

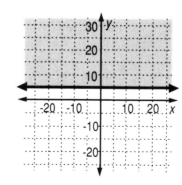

9. Write an equation for the line containing (3, 1) and (3, 5).

_____

10. Paul weighed himself every day for a week. Each time he weighed 145 lb. Using w for weight, write an equation satisfying this situation.

_____

NAME _____

LESSON **MASTER 7–3**
QUESTIONS ON **SPUR** OBJECTIVES

■**SKILLS**   *Objective A (See pages 360–363 for objectives.)*
In 1–6, simplify.

1. $|12 - 19|$ _____

2. $|6 - 81|$ _____

3. $|-219 - 31|$ _____

4. $|-7| + |-2|$ _____

5. $|18| - |-12|$ _____

6. ABS(-1.8 + 0.6) _____

■**REPRESENTATIONS**   *Objective G*
In 7–12, find the distance on a number line between the points with the given coordinates.

7. 237 and 182 _____

8. 12 and -2 _____

9. -32 and 14 _____

10. -0.64 and -0.42 _____

11. $\frac{-1}{2}$ and $\frac{-3}{4}$ _____

12. r and -25 _____

13. Find the perimeter of the rectangle at right.

_____

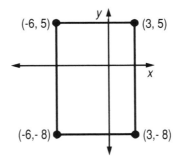

14. The distance between two points on a number line with coordinates $8F - 3$ and $3F + 9$ is 15. Find all possible values of F.

_____

■**REPRESENTATIONS**   *Objective L*
In 15–18, find and graph all solutions.

15. $|x - 13| < 4$ _____

16. $|y + 9| = 1.5$ _____

←————————————————→

←————————————————→

17. $|w - 4| > 8$ _____

18. $|y - 5| \le -2$ _____

←————————————————→

←————————————————→

Algebra © Scott, Foresman and Company

57

NAME _____

■**SKILLS**   *Objective B (See pages 360–363 for objectives.)*
In 1 and 2, a. approximate the square root to the nearest hundredth using your calculator. b. Show a check of your answer.

1. $\sqrt{1357}$ a. _____

2. $\sqrt{117}$ a. _____

   b. _____

   b. _____

In 3 and 4, find the two integers between which the square root lies.

3. $-\sqrt{87}$ _____ and _____

4. $\sqrt{103}$ _____ and _____

In 5–12, simplify.

5. $\sqrt{9 + 16}$ 6. $\sqrt{4 \cdot 9}$ 7. $\sqrt{9} + \sqrt{16}$

_____   _____   _____

8. $\sqrt{4} \cdot \sqrt{9}$ 9. $2 + \sqrt{\frac{18}{2}}$ 10. $7 - \sqrt{\frac{75}{3}}$

_____   _____   _____

11. $5\sqrt{8} \cdot \sqrt{8}$ 12. $-4\sqrt{13} \cdot \sqrt{13}$

_____   _____

13. Evaluate $35 - \sqrt{1 + 4n}$ when $n = 30$.   _____

14. Evaluate $4(7 + 2\sqrt{x})$ when $x = 25$.   _____

15. Evaluate $3(\sqrt{x})^2$ when $x = 3$.   _____

■**SKILLS**   *Objective C*
In 16–23, solve. Give the exact answer in simplified form.

16. $11n^2 = 187$ _____ 17. $-2a^2 = 32$ _____

18. $\frac{7}{m} = \frac{m}{5}$ _____ 19. $\frac{k}{7} = \frac{13}{k}$ _____

20. $\sqrt{y} - 9 = 25$ _____ 21. $4\sqrt{t} + 7 = 35$ _____

22. $2x^2 - 28 = 100$ _____ 23. $3y^2 + 10 = 157$ _____

■**USES**   *Objective F*
24. A side of a square is $5\sqrt{13}$ cm.
Find the area of the square.   _____

25. Four square tiles fit together to cover an area of
324 sq in. Find the length of the side of one tile.   _____

58

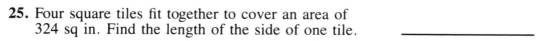

LESSON MASTER 7-5
QUESTIONS ON SPUR OBJECTIVES

■ **USES** *Objective F (See pages 360–363 for objectives.)*

1. A carpenter designs a brace for the corner of a frame as shown. Find the length c of the brace.

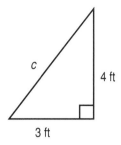

_____

2. A suitcase is 80 cm long and 50 cm wide. What is the length of the largest umbrella that can fit in the suitcase?

_____

3. Two boats leave a dock at the same time. One sails north at 9 mph, the other sails east at 10 mph. How far apart are they after 2 hours?

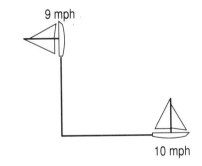

_____

4. Suppose you wanted to construct a ski lift that rises 50 m and extends a horizontal distance of 120 m. Ignoring the slack in the cable, what distance would the cable extend?

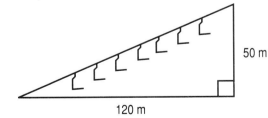

_____

LESSON **MASTER** 7–5
(page 2)

■**REPRESENTATIONS**   *Objective J*

5. Examine the right triangle at the right.

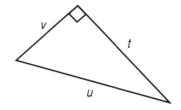

   a. What variables represent
   the lengths of the legs?

   _____

   b. What variable represents
   the length of the hypotenuse?

   _____

6. Find the value of c in the triangle at
the right.

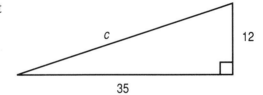

_____

7. Find the value of a in the triangle at
the right.

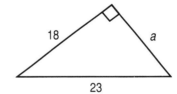

_____

8. Find the length of the hypotenuse
of the triangle at the right.

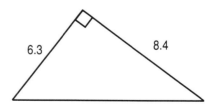

_____

9. The diagonal of a rectangle is 26 and one side is 10. Find the lengths of all
other sides.

_____ _____ _____

10. The diagonal of a square is $5\sqrt{2}$. Find the length of each side of the
square.

_____

Algebra © Scott, Foresman and Company

LESSON MASTER 7-6
QUESTIONS ON SPUR OBJECTIVES

■SKILLS   *Objective B (See pages 360–363 for objectives.)*
In 1–4, simplify. Use your calculator to check your answer.

1. $\sqrt{32}$ _____   **2.** $\sqrt{27}$ _____

3. $\sqrt{108}$ _____   **4.** $\sqrt{147}$ _____

5. Evaluate $\sqrt{3 + 23n}$
when $n = 3$.

6. Evaluate $\sqrt{64 - 7n}$
when $n = 2$.

_____   _____

■PROPERTIES   *Objective E*
In 7 and 8, solve. Simplify your answer.

7. $2x^2 = 24$ _____   **8.** $\dfrac{14}{m} = \dfrac{m}{7}$ _____

In 9–16, simplify.

9. $\sqrt{25 + 25}$ **10.** $\sqrt{72 + 72}$ **11.** $2\sqrt{48}$

_____   _____   _____

12. $3\sqrt{200}$ **13.** $\dfrac{\sqrt{52}}{2}$ **14.** $\dfrac{\sqrt{135}}{6}$

_____   _____   _____

15. $\sqrt{12} \cdot \sqrt{3} + \sqrt{8} \cdot \sqrt{2}$ _____   **16.** $\sqrt{50} \cdot \sqrt{8} - \sqrt{18} \cdot \sqrt{2}$ _____

In 17 and 18, simplify. Assume all variables are positive.

17. $\sqrt{25a^2b^2}$ _____   **18.** $\sqrt{81x^2y^2}$ _____

■USES   *Objective F*
19. Each side of a square is 9. Find the diagonal and simplify your answer.

_____

20. The sides of a rectangle are 6 and 15. Find the diagonal and simplify your answer.

_____

LESSON MASTER 7–7
QUESTIONS ON SPUR OBJECTIVES

■**REPRESENTATIONS**   *Objective K (See pages 360–363 for objectives.)*
In 1–6, use the graph at the right. The midpoint of *AC* is *M*. Determine
each length.

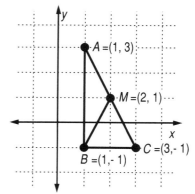

1. *AB*   _____

2. *CB*   _____

3. *AC*   _____

4. *BM*   _____

5. *MA*   _____

6. *MC*   _____

A = (1, 3)
M = (2, 1)
C = (3, -1)
B = (1, -1)

In 7–10, find *XY*.

7. *X* = (4, 9) and *Y* = (1, 5)   _____

8. *X* = (-3, 6) and *Y* = (2, -6)   _____

9. *X* = (-11, -16) and *Y* = (0, -20)   _____

10. *X* = (1.8, -2.4) and *Y* = (1.2, -1.6)   _____

In 11 and 12, use the diagram at the right. Each small square represents a city block.

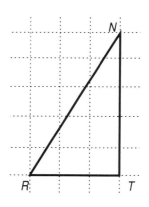

11. What is the street distance
between *R* and *N*?

_____

12. How far is it from *R* to *N* as the
crow flies?

_____

N
R   *T*

In 13–15, use the graph of the rectangle.

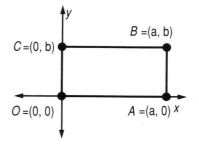

13. Find *OB*. _____

14. Find *AC*. _____

15. What can you conclude about the
diagonals of a rectangle?

_____

C = (0, b)   *B = (a, b)*
O = (0, 0)   *A = (a, 0)*

LESSON **MASTER 7–8**
QUESTIONS ON **SPUR** OBJECTIVES

■SKILLS *Objective D (See pages 360–363 for objectives.)*

1. If $4y = 5.1$, find $12y$. _____

2. If $3n + 1 = 11$, find $9n + 3$. _____

3. If $2x^2 = 9$, find $(2x^2)^2$. _____

4. If $\sqrt{5p - 1} = 7$, find $5p - 1$. _____

5. If $8k = 15$, find $16k - 1$. _____

6. If $-6s = 19$, find $12s + 5$. _____

7. If $3t + 6u = -3$, and $2u = -3$, find $3t$. _____

8. If $4f - 8g = 9$, and $2g = 1$, find $4f$. _____

In 9–12, simplify.

9. $7\sqrt{3} + 4\sqrt{3} - 6\sqrt{3} - 3\sqrt{3}$ _____

10. $4\sqrt{w + 5} + 13\sqrt{w + 5} - \sqrt{w + 5}$ _____

11. $12(x - 4) - 17(x - 4) - 2(x - 4)$ _____

12. $5(2y - 1)^2 - 8(2y - 1)^2 + 3(2y - 1)^2$ _____

In 13–20, solve.

13. $(t + 3)^2 = 9$ _____

14. $(d - 4)^2 = 49$ _____

15. $\sqrt{3y - 2} = 5$ _____

16. $\sqrt{4p + 5} = 9$ _____

17. $|3w + 7| = 22$ _____

18. $|11q - 4| = 29$ _____

19. $\dfrac{x + 1}{2} = \dfrac{8}{x + 1}$ _____

20. $\dfrac{9}{3x - 3} = \dfrac{3x - 3}{4}$ _____

Algebra © Scott, Foresman and Company

63

LESSON **MASTER 8–1**

QUESTIONS ON **SPUR** OBJECTIVES

■**USES**   *Objective G (See pages 418–421 for objectives.)*

In 1–4, use the data given below on number of deaths in the U.S. caused by home fires.

Year	No. Deaths	Year	No. Deaths
1950	5000	1970	5600
1955	5400	1975	5000
1960	6350	1980	4400
1965	6100		

1. Graph the situation on the axes below.

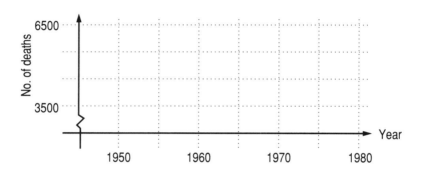

2. Find the rate of change of deaths per year from 1950 to 1955.   _____

3. a. In which five-year period did the number of deaths increase the most?   _____

   b. What was the rate of change of deaths per year for that period?   _____

4. a. In which two five-year periods was the rate of change the same?   _____

   b. What was the average rate of change of deaths per year in those periods?   _____

5. Using only the trend shown by the data for 1960–1980, predict an estimate for the number of deaths in the U.S. caused by home fires in 1985.   _____

Algebra © Scott, Foresman and Company

LESSON **MASTER** 8–2
QUESTIONS ON **SPUR** OBJECTIVES

■**SKILLS**   *Objective A (See pages 418–421 for objectives.)*
In 1–4, find the slope of the line through the given points.
  1. (2, -4), (5, -1)   **2.** (12, 3), (2, 7)

  _____   _____

  3. (-5.2, 3.7), (7.2, 4.1)   **4.** (4, *k*), (-2, *k*)

  _____   _____

  5. Determine whether the points (3, -1), (5, 2),
       (9, 8) lie on the same line. If they do, give the
       slope of that line.   _____

■**PROPERTIES**   *Objective D*

  6. If the slope of a line is ___?___ , then as *x*
       increases, *y* decreases.   _____

  7. Consider lines ℓ, *m,* and *n* graphed at right.
       a. Which line has slope -2?

       _____

       b. Which line has slope -$\frac{1}{3}$?

       _____

       c. Which line has slope 0?

       _____

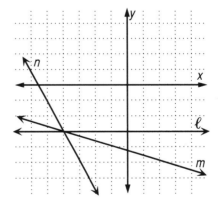

■**PROPERTIES**   *Objective F*
In 8–10, find the slope of the line with the given equation.
  8. 2*x* + *y* = 6   **9.** 5*x* − 2*y* = 10   **10.** *x* = 8

  _____   _____   _____

■**REPRESENTATIONS**   *Objective I*
11. Graph the line which passes
       through (0, 1) and has a slope
       of -2.

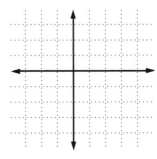

NAME _____

LESSON **MASTER 8–3**
QUESTIONS ON **SPUR** OBJECTIVES

■**PROPERTIES** *Objective D* *(See pages 418–421 for objectives.)*
1. Why does the line through (4, 1) and (4, -2) not have a
slope?

_____

_____

■**REPRESENTATIONS** *Objective I*
2. A roof rises 6 inches for
each 12 inches of
horizontal distance.
Calculate the slope of
this roof and picture it at
right. _____

**In 3–6, graph the line passing through the given point and having the
given slope.**

3. (-2, 1), slope $\frac{1}{2}$

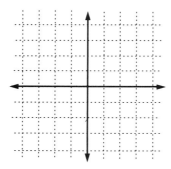

4. (4, 2), slope -2

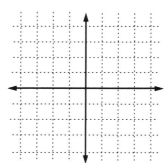

5. (-1, -3), slope $\frac{1}{5}$

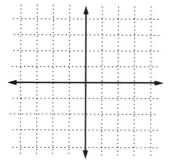

6. (0, -2), slope $-\frac{2}{3}$

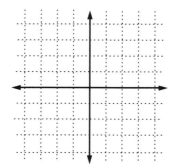

7. Name one other point on the line
through (-5, 2) with slope 2.

_____

8. Name one other point on the line
through (0, $-\frac{1}{2}$) with slope $\frac{3}{2}$.

_____

66

Algebra © Scott, Foresman and Company

LESSON MASTER 8–4
QUESTIONS ON SPUR OBJECTIVES

■SKILLS   *Objective B (See pages 418–421 for objectives.)*
In 1–4, write an equation for the line with the given slope *m* and *y*-intercept *b*.

1. $m = 3, b = -1$

2. $m = 11.2, b = -3.9$

_____

3. $m = -3.2, b = 0$

4. $m = 4, b = p$

_____

■PROPERTIES   *Objective E*
In 5–8, write each equation in slope-intercept form.

5. $8x = 13 - 2y$

6. $5x + 3y = -2$

_____

7. $x - y = 2$

8. $y = 5$

_____

■PROPERTIES   *Objective F*
In 9–11, find the slope and the *y*-intercept of the given line.

9. $y = -2$ slope _____   *y*-intercept _____

10. $2x - 8y = 11$ slope _____   *y*-intercept _____

11. $x = 23$ slope _____   *y*-intercept _____

■USES   *Objective H*
12. For an increase of one Kelvin *(K)*, the Fahrenheit temperature *(F)* goes up 1.8 degrees. If $F = 32°$ when $K = 273.15$, write an equation for *F* in terms of *K*.

_____

■REPRESENTATIONS   *Objective I*
13. Graph the line which passes through (-2,4) and has a slope of -2.

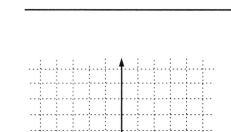

LESSON **MASTER** 8–5
QUESTIONS ON **SPUR** OBJECTIVES

■**SKILLS**   *Objective B* *(See pages 418–421 for objectives.)*
In 1–8, given one point and slope, find an equation for the line.

1. point (4, -4), slope -3

2. point (-3, 1), slope $\frac{2}{3}$

_____

_____

3. point (2.5, 6), slope 0.8

4. point (-15, 0), slope $-\frac{3}{5}$

_____

_____

5. point (5, -9), slope 0

6. point (5, 8), slope undefined

_____

_____

7. point $(0, \frac{1}{2})$, slope $-\frac{1}{8}$

8. point (0, -3), slope 4

_____

_____

■**USES**   *Objective H*

9. A repairperson charges $25 per hour plus an initial service-call charge. The bill for 3 hours was $105. Give a linear equation which relates the cost y of having the repairperson work x hours.

_____

10. Rich Nomore has been spending 65 cents on bus fare each day from a coin wallet. After 12 days, he has $4.70 left. Write an equation giving the amount y he had left after x days.

_____

11. It costs $1.25 for a 3-minute call and 30¢ for each additional minute. Give the cost c for a m-minute call, when $m > 3$.

_____

12. There are 100 days gone of the school year and 40,000 sheets of duplicating paper are left. If about 2,000 sheets are used each day, how many sheets s were left after d days of school?

_____

Algebra © Scott, Foresman and Company

LESSON **MASTER** **8–6**
QUESTIONS ON **SPUR** OBJECTIVES

■SKILLS *Objective C (See pages 418–421 for objectives.)*
In 1–6, find an equation for the line through the two given points.

1. $(4, -1), (7, 5)$

2. $(204, 358), (300, 406)$

3. $(-0.43, 1.8), (0.57, -3.6)$

4. $\left(\frac{2}{3}, \frac{3}{2}\right), \left(\frac{5}{6}, \frac{3}{4}\right)$

5. $(0, 0), (1, \sqrt{2})$

6. $(a, 0), (0, b)$

7. a. Find an equation for the line through $(-3, -8)$ and $(1, 1)$.

b. Does the point $(9, 19)$ lie on the line?

■USES *Objective H*

8. A linear equation can be used to describe the length of a spring, y, when it is stretched by a weight, x. A spring is 4 cm long when a 50-g weight is attached, and 6 cm long when a 74-g weight is attached. Write an equation which relates x and y.

9. A man whose foot is 12 in. long wears a size 12 shoe. A man whose foot is 10 in. long wears a size 6 shoe. If the shoe size, S, and the foot length, F, are linearly related, write an equation which describes that relation.

10. a. Harvey began his diet when he weighed 260 pounds. After four weeks he weighed 246 pounds. If he lost weight at a constant rate, write an equation which relates his weight, W, and the number of weeks on the diet, n.

b. Why doesn't this relation work when n is large?

LESSON **MASTER** 8–7
QUESTIONS ON **SPUR** OBJECTIVES

■**REPRESENTATIONS** *Objective J (See pages 418–421 for objectives.)*
1. Below is a table showing the median height in cm of boys in the U.S. by age.

Age	Height (cm)	Age	Height (cm)	Age	Height (cm)
2	87	8	127	14	163
3	95	9	132	15	169
4	103	10	138	16	174
5	110	11	143	17	176
6	116	12	150	18	177
7	122	13	160		

a. Graph this data, and sketch a line to fit the data.

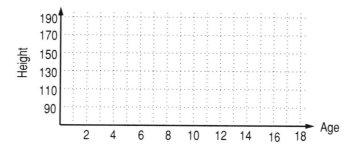

b. Find an equation for the line. _____

2. The table below gives the life expectancy of the average person at birth in the U.S. for the years 1900–1980.

Year	Expectancy	Year	Expectancy
1900	47.3	1950	68.2
1910	50.0	1960	69.7
1920	54.1	1970	70.8
1930	59.7	1980	73.8
1940	62.9		

a. Graph this data, and sketch a line to fit the data.

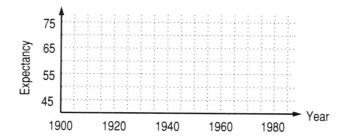

b. Find an equation for the line. _____

c. What life expectancy would you predict in 1990? _____

70

LESSON **MASTER 8-8**
QUESTIONS ON **SPUR** OBJECTIVES

■**PROPERTIES**   *Objective E (See pages 418–421 for objectives.)*
In 1–6, rewrite the equation in slope-intercept form.

1. $5x + 2y = 10$

2. $6x = 16 - 3y$

_____

3. $-15x + 7y = 14$

4. $-7x = 6 - 13y$

_____

5. $2x + y = -6$

6. $12x = -15 - 3y$

_____

In 7–12, rewrite the equation in standard form with integer coefficients.

7. $1.1x = .2y + 9$

8. $0.6y = 0.7x - 2$

_____

9. $\frac{2}{3}x - \frac{3}{4}y - 1 = 0$

10. $y = -\frac{4}{3}x - 1$

_____

11. $5.5x - 3y = 1.0$

12. $0.6x = 1.6 - 5.3y$

_____

■**USES**   *Objective H*
13. Tickets for the concert are \$6 and \$4. If *s* six-dollar tickets and *f* four-dollar tickets were sold and \$1000 was taken in, **a.** give a possible pair of values of *s* and *f* and **b.** write an equation relating *s* and *f*.

a. _____   **b.** _____

14. Paula worked for *x* hours at \$4 an hour and *y* hours at time and a half. She earned a total of \$48. Write an equation that relates *x* and *y*.

_____

LESSON **MASTER** **8–9**
QUESTIONS ON **SPUR** OBJECTIVES

■**REPRESENTATIONS**   *Objective K (See pages 418–421 for objectives.)*
In 1–6, graph the inequality.

1. $y \geq 2x - 3$

2. $y < -\frac{x}{2} + 1$

3. $4x - 3y < 6$

4. $2x - 6y \geq 0$

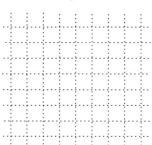

5. $5x + 3y \leq 0$

6. $y - 3 < 0$

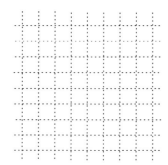

In 7 and 8, a. write an inequality to fit each situation, and b. draw the graph.

7. For a performance, adult tickets are $5 and children's tickets are $3. To make a profit, at least $2000 must be collected. The ticket sales were a adult and c children's tickets.

a.

b.

8. Henry plans to buy x 25-cent stamps and y 20-cent stamps. He has $7.50 to spend, but does not need to spend all of it.

a.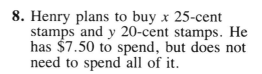

b.

Algebra © Scott, Foresman and Company

NAME _____

LESSON **MASTER** 9–1
QUESTIONS ON **SPUR** OBJECTIVES

■**USES** *Objective F (See pages 471–473 for objectives.)*
In 1–4, find the amount for each of the following bank accounts after one year for the given principal and annual yield.

1. $100, 5.5%

2. $240, 6%

_____

_____

3. $1200, 7.5%

4. $2500, 8.4%

_____

_____

5. Suppose *P* dollars is invested in a Certificate of Deposit (CD) with an annual yield of 7.2% for 3 years. Write an expression for the amount received when the CD matures.

_____

6. Petra opened a savings account by depositing $800. If the annual yield is 5.8%, write an expression for the amount in the account after *n* years.

_____

In 7 and 8, find the amount in an account from the given information.

7. $400 at 5.7% after 3 years

8. $2200 at 7.8% after 2 years

_____

_____

In 9 and 10, find the interest earned from the given information.

9. $180 at 5% for 2 years

10. $1 at 6% for 4 years

_____

_____

11. a. Which will earn more interest, $120 at 4% for 2 years or $120 at 8% for 1 year?

_____

b. By how much do the earnings differ?

_____

12. If $200 is deposited in an account with an annual yield of 10%, in how many years will the amount double?

_____

13. In 1626, Peter Minuit bought Manhattan Island from the Manhattan Indians for beads, clothing, and trinkets worth about $24. If that money had been invested at 5% annual yield, what would the amount be in 1988?

_____

LESSON **MASTER 9–2**
QUESTIONS ON **SPUR** OBJECTIVES

■SKILLS   *Objective A*   *(See pages 471–473 for objectives.)*
In 1–9, evaluate.

1. 2^4 _____

2. -2^4 _____

3. $(-2)^4$ _____

4. $4 \cdot 17^0$ _____

5. -5^3 _____

6. $(-5)^3$ _____

7. If $x = -4$, then $10 + x^0 =$ _____ .

8. $3 \cdot 10^2 + 6 \cdot 10^1 + 8 \cdot 10^0$ _____

9. $8 \cdot 10^0 + 2 \cdot 10^1 + 1 \cdot 10^2$ _____

■PROPERTIES   *Objective E*
In 10 and 11, tell whether the statement is true or false. If false, correct the statement by changing the right side of the equation.

10. $12 + x^0 = 12$ _____

11. If $x = 3$ and $y = 2$, then $(x + y)^0 = 1$.   _____

■USES   *Objective G*

12. Suppose that 10 squirrels are introduced to an area. If their population doubles every three months, how many squirrels are there in 1 year?

_____

13. The number of people who ride skateboards in a town is growing at the rate of 20% per year. If 400 ride skateboards now and the growth rate remains constant, how many will ride skateboards in 3 years?

_____

14. A gray filter lets in only $\frac{2}{5}$ of the light that hits it. What fraction (or portion) of the light would pass through a series of 3 of these filters?

_____

15. A copy machine can make an enlargement 1.2 times as large as the original. If you make copies of copies, enlarging each time, how many times as large as the original will the fourth copy be?

_____

74   *Algebra* © Scott, Foresman and Company

LESSON **MASTER** 9–3
QUESTIONS ON **SPUR** OBJECTIVES

■**USES**   *Objective G (See pages 471–473 for objectives.)*

1. A 6″ by 4″ drawing is reduced three times by using a photocopy machine. Each time it is reduced to 90% of its previous dimensions. What is its final size?

_____

2. Suppose a radioactive substance loses $\frac{1}{2}$ of its remaining mass each second. How much of a 36 g sample will remain after 6 seconds?

_____

3. Each year an automobile depreciates in value by 25%. Find the value after five years of a car which cost $4800 new.

_____

4. Because of the use of an antibiotic, 15% of the bacteria die each hour. After how many hours will less than 50% of the original bacteria remain alive?

_____

5. The population of a large city has been decreasing 2% each year. At this rate, what will be the percent of loss in a decade?

_____

6. The enrollment at a certain college is increasing at the rate of 2% per year. If there are presently 1752 students, how many will there be in 10 years?

_____

LESSON **MASTER** **9–4**
QUESTIONS ON **SPUR** OBJECTIVES

■**REPRESENTATIONS**   *Objective I (See pages 471–473 for objectives.)*
In 1–4, tell whether the graph of each equation is linear or exponential.

1. $y = 2x + 5$

2. $y = 20 - .06x$

3. $y = 20(.06)^x$

4. $y = 2(1.05)^x$

5. When x is large and increases, for which equation does y increase more rapidly?

(a) $y = 24 + 6x$ (b) $y = 24(1.06)^x$ _____

In 6–9, match each equation with its graph.

6. $y = 10 - 5x$ _____

7. $y = 10(1.5)^x$ _____

8. $y = 10 + 5x$ _____

9. $y = 10(0.5)^x$ _____

(a)
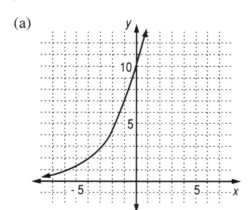

(b)
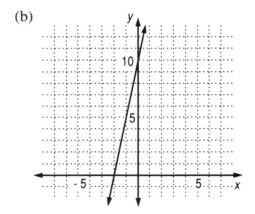

(c)
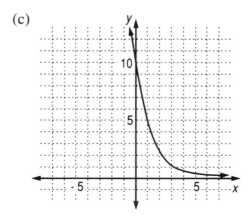

(d)
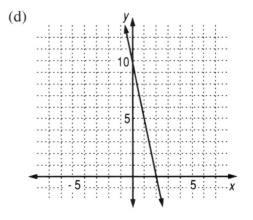

LESSON MASTER 9-4
(page 2)

In 10 and 11, graph.

10. $y = 3^x$ for $-3 \leq x \leq 3$

11. $y = 0.5^x$ for $-3 \leq x \leq 3$

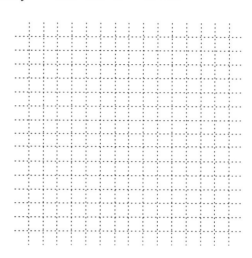

12. $1000 is invested in a savings account at an 8% annual yield.

a. Complete the table below for the amount in the account after 0, 2, 4, 6, and 8 years.

Year	0	2	4	6	8
Amount Saved					

b. Graph the situation.

c. Approximately how much is in the account after 5 years?

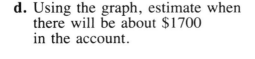

_____

d. Using the graph, estimate when there will be about $1700 in the account.

_____

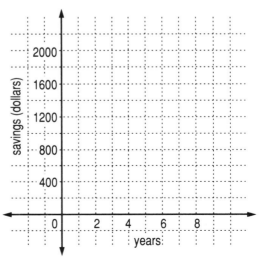

NAME _____

LESSON **MASTER** 9–5
QUESTIONS ON **SPUR** OBJECTIVES

■SKILLS *Objective A (See pages 471–473 for objectives.)*

1. Evaluate $3^2 \cdot 3^3$. _____

2. Evaluate $(3^2)^3$. _____

3. Find the value of $x^3 \cdot x^4$ when $x = 2$. _____

4. Find the value of $(2y)^5$ when $y = -1$. _____

■SKILLS *Objective B*
In 5–18, simplify.

5. $a^5 \cdot a^7$ _____

6. $2n^0 \cdot n^8$ _____

7. $6t^6 \cdot 3t^2$ _____

8. $0.7b^3 \cdot 0.4b^9$ _____

9. $u^7 \cdot v^2 \cdot u^6 \cdot v^4$ _____

10. $g^5 \cdot k^3 \cdot g^8 \cdot k^9$ _____

11. $(b^6c^5)(b^2c^6)$ _____

12. $(w^5)^2$ _____

13. $3(h^4)^3$ _____

14. $(3h^4)^3$ _____

15. $(x^4)^2(x^4)^2$ _____

16. $(x^2)^4 + (x^4)^2$ _____

17. $(a + b)^4(a + b)^5$ _____

18. $(2s - 3t)^3(2s - 3t)^8$ _____

■PROPERTIES *Objective E*
In 19–22, name the property or properties which justify each statement.

19. $r^9r^6 = r^{15}$ _____

20. $(4d^3)d^2 = 4d^5$ _____

_____

21. $(a^8)^4 = a^{32}$ _____

In 22–25, tell whether the statement is true or false. If false, correct the statement by changing the right side of the equation.

22. $(p^3)^4 = p^7$

23. $q^5 \cdot q^3 = q^8$

_____   _____

24. $(5^3)^0 = 0$

25. $3x^2 \cdot 2x^3 = 5x^5$

_____   _____

78

Algebra © Scott, Foresman and Company

LESSON MASTER 9–6
QUESTIONS ON **SPUR** OBJECTIVES

■SKILLS *Objective A* *(See pages 471–473 for objectives.)*
In 1–6, evaluate.

1. 5^{-1} _____

2. 10^{-4} _____

3. $7 \cdot 4^{-3}$ _____

4. $-9 \cdot 3^{-3}$ _____

5. -2^{-6} _____

6. $(-2)^{-6}$ _____

In 7–10, simplify.

7. $3 \cdot 10^1 + 1 \cdot 10^0 + 4 \cdot 10^{-1}$ _____

8. $7 \cdot 10^0 + 2 \cdot 10^{-1} + 6 \cdot 10^{-3}$ _____

9. $8 \cdot 10^4 + 5 \cdot 10^0 + 9 \cdot 10^{-1}$ _____

10. $8^{17} \cdot 8^{-17}$ _____

■SKILLS *Objective B*
In 11–18, rewrite without a negative exponent.

11. xy^{-3} _____

12. $2a^{-4}$ _____

13. $3t^5$ _____

14. $(b^7)^{-2}$ _____

15. $(4y)^{-1}$ _____

16. m^6n^{-3} _____

17. $a^3b^{-2}c^4$ _____

18. $w^{-6}x^2y^{-5}$ _____

■PROPERTIES *Objective E*
In 19 and 20, name the property or properties which justify each statement.

19. $x^5y^{-1} = \dfrac{x^5}{y}$ _____

20. $(a^3)^{-2} = \dfrac{1}{a^6}$ _____

_____

■USES *Objective H*

21. The population of a town is 25,194. It has been gaining 8% for each of the last three years. What was the population three years ago? _____

22. Hakeem has $2917 in a Certificate of Deposit which has an annual yield of 5%. How much was it worth 4 years ago? _____

LESSON **MASTER** **9–7**
QUESTIONS ON **SPUR** OBJECTIVES

■SKILLS   *Objective A (See pages 471–473 for objectives.)*
In 1–6, evaluate.

1. $\dfrac{3^5}{3^8}$ _____

2. $\dfrac{7^{12}}{7^8}$ _____

3. $\dfrac{2^x}{2^x}$ _____

4. $\dfrac{6^{-8}}{6^{-9}}$ _____

5. $\dfrac{5.6 \cdot 10^{15}}{3.2 \cdot 10^{10}}$ _____

6. $\dfrac{1.21 \cdot 10^6}{8.8 \cdot 10^9}$ _____

7. Rewrite $\dfrac{2187}{27} = 81$ using positive powers of 3. _____

■SKILLS   *Objective B*
In 8–17, simplify.

8. $\dfrac{8a^8b^3}{2a^4b^2}$ _____

9. $\dfrac{15r^4s}{25r^2s^5} \cdot r^3$ _____

10. $\dfrac{(h + 2k)^5}{(h + 2k)^2}$ _____

11. $\dfrac{(y - 8)^6}{(y - 8)^8}$ _____

12. $\dfrac{w^{18n}}{w^{22n}}$ _____

13. $\dfrac{z^{12k} \cdot z^{3k}}{z^{8k}}$ _____

14. $\dfrac{t^7}{t^{-2} \cdot t^0}$ _____

15. $\dfrac{v^{-5}}{v^{-10}}$ _____

16. $\dfrac{4x^6 + 3x^6}{x^6}$ _____

17. $\dfrac{9y^3 - 3y^3}{3y^3}$ _____

■PROPERTIES   *Objective E*
In 18 and 19, tell whether the statement is true or false.

18. $\dfrac{a^{16}}{a^8} = a^2$ _____

19. $\dfrac{c^{9n}}{c^{3n}} = c^{6n}$ _____

■USES   *Objective H*
20. In 1981, there were about $1.6 \cdot 10^8$ registered vehicles (autos, buses, trucks) in the U.S. If there were $1.12 \cdot 10^{11}$ gallons of fuel consumed, how many gallons per vehicle was this?

_____

21. In 1986, $1.93 \cdot 10^{10}$ pounds of beef were consumed in the U.S. If at the end of 1986 the U.S. population was 242.2 million people, how many pounds per person was this?

_____

Algebra © Scott, Foresman and Company

LESSON **MASTER** 9-8
QUESTIONS ON **SPUR** OBJECTIVES

■**SKILLS**   *Objective A* *(See pages 471–473 for objectives.)*
In 1–4, evaluate.

1. 2^3 _____ **2.** 3^2 _____ **3.** $(-2)^4$ _____ **4.** -2^4 _____

■**SKILLS**   *Objective C*
In 5–24, simplify.

5. $(2a)^3$ _____ **6.** $(3x^3)^2$ _____

7. $5(4y)^2$ _____ **8.** $7(b^5)^3$ _____

9. $\left(\dfrac{t}{2}\right)^4$ _____ **10.** $\left(\dfrac{2w^2}{3}\right)^5$ _____

11. $\left(\dfrac{k^5}{3}\right)^4$ _____ **12.** $\left(\dfrac{2b^4c^7}{5}\right)^2$ _____

13. $(2.5y^2)^3$ _____ **14.** $0.61(3c^5)^4$ _____

15. $(r^m)^n$ _____ **16.** $(2x^a)^0$ _____

17. $\left(\dfrac{a}{b}\right)^n$ _____ **18.** $\left(\dfrac{x^n}{y^2}\right)^3$ _____

■**PROPERTIES**   *Objective E*
In 19 and 20, name the property which justifies the statement.

19. $\left(\dfrac{x}{y}\right)^5 = \dfrac{x^5}{y^5}$ _____

20. $(a^m b^n)^3 = a^{3m}b^{3n}$ _____

■**USES**   *Objective H*
21. A square section of land is one mile on a side. (Recall that there are $5.28 \cdot 10^3$ feet in a mile.) What is the area of the section in square feet?

_____

22. The planet Mercury, shaped nearly like a sphere, has a diameter of about 3031 miles. What is the volume of Mercury in cubic miles? (Recall that the volume of a sphere is $\frac{4}{3}\pi r^3$.)

_____

LESSON **MASTER** 9–9
QUESTIONS ON **SPUR** OBJECTIVES

■SKILLS *Objective A (See pages 471–473 for objectives.)*
In 1–4, choose the best answer, then check it by testing a special case.

1. $n^2 n^3 =$ _____

   (a) n^6 (b) n^5 (c) n^9 (d) n^1

2. $(n^2)^3 =$ _____

   (a) n^6 (b) n^5 (c) n^9 (d) n^1

3. $\dfrac{x^6}{x^2} =$ _____

   (a) x^8 (b) x^{12} (c) x^3 (d) x^4

4. $\left(\dfrac{x^a}{x^b}\right)^{-1} =$ _____

   (a) x^{b-a} (b) x^{a-b} (c) $x^{\frac{a}{b}}$ (d) $x^{\frac{b}{a}}$

■PROPERTIES *Objective D*
In 5–8, a. find a value of the variable for which the pattern is true; b. find a value for which the pattern is false.

5. $x^2 + x^2 = x^4$

   a. _____

   b. _____

6. $(x^2)^3 = x^5$

   a. _____

   b. _____

7. $(a + b)^2 = a^2 + b^2$

   a. _____

   b. _____

8. $2^x = x^2$

   a. _____

   b. _____

9. Jason claimed that $x^2 + x + 1$ is a prime number for any nonzero whole number x.

   a. Find at least 3 numbers for which he is right.   _____, _____, _____

   b. Find a counterexample.   _____

NAME _____

LESSON MASTER 10–1
QUESTIONS ON **SPUR** OBJECTIVES

■**SKILLS**   *Objective A (See pages 527–529 for objectives.)*
In 1–3, classify each polynomial as a monomial, binomial, or trinomial.
  1. $4 - 3x$ **2.** $3ab$ **3.** $4n^2 - 3n + 2$

_____   _____   _____

In 4–6, give the degree of each polynomial.
  4. $17 - 6y$ **5.** $3t^2 - 5t + 7t^3 - 10$ **6.** $4x^2$

_____   _____   _____

In 7 and 8, write the polynomial in descending order of exponents.
  7. $12 + 2x^3 - 4x^2 + x^5$ **8.** $8y - 6y^2 + 5 + 3y^3$

_____   _____

In 9 and 10, evaluate.
  9. $6x^2 - 2x + 1$ when $x = -3$ **10.** $8a^3 - 4a^2 + 3a - 2$ when $a = \frac{1}{2}$

_____   _____

■**USES**   *Objective I*
11. For three consecutive years, Mr. Sandberg's annual deposits in his
Individual Retirement Account (IRA) were $1000, $1500, and $2000. If
the account had an annual yield of 8%, how much did he have in his
account at the end of the third year?

_____

12. At each annual baseball card show, Tim buys baseball cards. The first year
he spent $20, the second, $30, the third, $50, and the fourth, $50. If the
value of the cards in his collection increases by 10% each year, how much
will the collection be worth at the end of the fourth year?

_____

13. If a ball is thrown upward at 57 ft/sec from a height of 3 ft, its distance s
above the ground after t seconds is given by the formula $s = -16t^2 + 57t + 3$. How far above the ground will it be

  a. after 2 seconds?   _____

  b. after 3 seconds?   _____

  c. Why is it lower after 3 seconds
    than after 2 seconds?   _____

LESSON **MASTER   10-2**
QUESTIONS ON **SPUR** OBJECTIVES

■SKILLS   *Objective A (See pages 527–529 for objectives.)*
In 1–8, simplify.

1. $(h - 3) + (2h + 6)$

2. $(3h^2 + 7h - 6) + (4h - 9)$

_____

3. $(16 - 7x^2) + (9 - 4x + 2x^2)$

4. $(4t - 9) - (3t + 8)$

_____

5. $(9r - 7) - (3r - 4) - (r - 6)$

6. $(11 - 5w^2) - (18 - 8w^2)$

_____

7. $(10k^2 - 5k + 32) - (2k^2 - 3k + 6)$ _____

8. $(4y^4 + 6y^3 - 5y^2 - 11y) + (y^4 - y^3 + 12y)$ _____

■USES   *Objective I*

9. Jack has two accounts, each with an annual scale factor of y. In one account he deposits \$150 a year, and in the other account he deposits \$250 a year.
a. How much does he have in both accounts combined after four years?

_____

b. If each account pays 7% interest, what is the total after four years?

_____

10. If a rocket is shot upward from the surface of the earth at 500 ft/sec, its distance s above the ground after t seconds is given by $s = 500t - 16t^2$. If a rocket is shot upward from the surface of the moon, then $s = 500t - 2.7t^2$. For the times that the rocket is actually in flight, how many feet higher will it go on the moon than on the earth after t seconds?

_____

■REPRESENTATIONS   *Objective J*
In 11 and 12, write an expression for the shaded area. Each quadrilateral shown is a rectangle.

11.

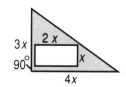

12.

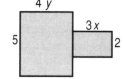

_____

Algebra © Scott, Foresman and Company

LESSON **MASTER** 10–3
QUESTIONS ON **SPUR** OBJECTIVES

■SKILLS *Objective B (See pages 527–529 for objectives.)*
In 1–6, multiply.

1. $6(x - 3x^2)$

2. $4r(r^2 + 2r + 3)$

_____

3. $(4y - 11)(-3x)$

4. $-5a(2a^2 - 3a - 10)$

_____

5. $\frac{1}{6}a^2(2a^2 - 3b^2)$

6. $-6xy(2x - 8y^3)$

_____

■USES *Objective I*

7. Gilbert received $110 on his 16th birthday, $140 on his 17th birthday, and $155 on his 18th birthday, which he invested after every birthday at a scale factor x. He kept his money invested at the same scale factor for 3 more years after his 18th birthday. How much money did he have at the end of this period?

_____

8. If Gilbert invests the amount in Question 7 at a different scale factor y, how much will he have after three more years?

_____

■REPRESENTATIONS *Objective J*
Refer to the diagram at the right.
9. a. Find the area of the shaded region.

_____

b. The shaded region is the amount of usable space on each floor of a building. If a company rents three full floors, how much space will the company have?

_____

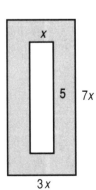

LESSON **MASTER** **10–4**
QUESTIONS ON **SPUR** OBJECTIVES

■**SKILLS**   *Objective D* *(See pages 527–529 for objectives.)*
In 1–5, fill in the blanks.

1. $6x^2 + 18x = 6x(\underline{\hspace{1cm}} + \underline{\hspace{1cm}})$ 2. $4y^2 - 6y = 2y(\underline{\hspace{1cm}} - \underline{\hspace{1cm}})$

3. $-8a^3 - 4a = -4a(\underline{\hspace{1cm}} + \underline{\hspace{1cm}})$ 4. $-9n^4 - 6n^2 = -3n^2(\underline{\hspace{1cm}} + \underline{\hspace{1cm}})$

5. $12n^3 - 21n^2 + 27n = 3n(\underline{\hspace{1cm}} - \underline{\hspace{1cm}} + \underline{\hspace{1cm}})$

In 6 and 7, find the largest common factor.

6. $-24b^3x,\ 32b^4x,\ 48b^2$ 7. $14r^2s^2,\ 63r^3s,\ -42r^2s^3$

_____   _____

In 8–13, factor.
8. $2k^5 + 3k^3$ 9. $6x^2 + 3$

_____   _____

10. $12c^3 - 15ac^2 - 18c$ 11. $x^3y^2 - x^2y^3 + x^2y^2$

_____   _____

12. $-3y^2z - 9yz - 12z$ 13. $25p^4q^3 + 20p^3q^4 - 35p^2q^3$

_____   _____

In 14–17, simplify.

14. $\dfrac{3a^2 + a}{a}$ 15. $\dfrac{16t^2 - 8t}{4t}$

_____   _____

16. $\dfrac{4d^3 - 6d^2 + 2d}{2d}$ 17. $\dfrac{9f^3 + 6f^2}{3f^2}$

_____   _____

86

Algebra © Scott, Foresman and Company

NAME _____

LESSON **MASTER 10–5**
QUESTIONS ON **SPUR** OBJECTIVES

■**SKILLS**   *Objective B (See pages 527–529 for objectives.)*
In 1–12, multiply and simplify.

1. $(x + 4)(x - 6)$

2. $(2a - 8)(a - 5)$

3. $(5r + 4)(3r + 2)$

4. $(11k - 3)(2k + 9)$

5. $(7x + 2y)(3x + 4y)$

6. $(x^2 + 2)(x^2 - 3)$

7. $(2y - 1)(y^2 - 3y - 1)$

8. $(a + b + 1)(a - b - 1)$

9. $(2x - y + 3)(x - y - 1)$

10. $(t^2 - 1)(t^4 + t^2 + 1)$

11. $(P^3 - 2)(P^3 - 1)$

12. $(a + 1)(a - 3)(a + 4)$

■**REPRESENTATIONS**   *Objective J*
**In 13 and 14, write the area of the largest rectangle as a. the sum of terms
and b. as the product of two polynomials.**

13. a. _____

b. _____

14. a. _____

b. _____

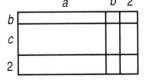

LESSON MASTER 10–6
QUESTIONS ON SPUR OBJECTIVES

■SKILLS   *Objective B (See pages 527–529 for objectives.)*
In 1–14, multiply and simplify.

1. $(x + 4)(x + 1)$

2. $(a - 4)(a - 3)$

3. $(2w - 3)(w + 5)$

4. $(5t + 3)(3t - 5)$

5. $(9a + 2b)(3a + b)$

6. $(7x - y)(x - y)$

7. $(x + y)(x + y)$

8. $(2y - z)(2y - z)$

9. $(r + s)(r - s)$

10. $(4d - 1)(4d + 1)$

11. $(x^2 + 1)(x^2 - 2)$

12. $(A^2 + 4)(A^2 + 3)$

13. $2y(2y - 1)(y - 3)$

14. $(a - 2)(a + 2)(a + 1)$

■USES   *Objective I*

15. Cindy can wear any of s sweaters or b blouses, with j jeans or k skirts. How many outfits are possible?

16. On a restaurant menu, you may select one item from m meats and f fish. You may also select one item from a second list of v vegetables and p potatoes. How many different meals can you order?

LESSON **MASTER 10–7**
QUESTIONS ON **SPUR** OBJECTIVES

■**SKILLS**   *Objective B (See pages 527–529 for objectives.)*
In 1–8, expand and simplify.

1. $(t + 3)^2$

2. $(r - 5)^2$

_____

3. $(3x + 4)^2$

4. $(10x - y)^2$

_____

5. $(7 - 2a)^2$

6. $3(2k - 1)^2$

_____

7. $2x(x + 3)^2$

8. $y^2 - (y - 6)^2$

_____

9. Show that $(a - 5)^2$ and $(5 - a)^2$ are equal.

_____

_____

_____

_____

■**PROPERTIES**   *Objective F*
In 10–15, show how to calculate in your head by using the square of a binomial.

10. 51^2 _____

11. 19^2 _____

12. $(1.02)^2$ _____

13. $(0.98)^2$ _____

14. 201^2 _____

15. 103^2 _____

LESSON MASTER 10–8
QUESTIONS ON SPUR OBJECTIVES

■SKILLS   *Objective C* *(See pages 527–529 for objectives.)*
In 1–4, determine if the number is a perfect square.

1. 262 _____   **2.** 289 _____   **3.** 123 _____   **4.** 200 _____

In 5–10, state whether the trinomial is a perfect square trinomial.

5. $x^2 + 4x + 4$ **6.** $2y^2 - 6y + 9$ **7.** $36a^2 - 30a + 25$

_____   _____   _____

8. $49t^2 + 42t - 9$ **9.** $4n^2 - 36nk + 81k^2$ **10.** $144x^2 + 24xy + y^2$

_____   _____   _____

■SKILLS   *Objective E*
In 11–18, write each perfect square trinomial as the square of a binomial. Otherwise, write "not a perfect square."

11. $w^2 + 18w + 81$ **12.** $9a^2 - 12a + 4$

_____   _____

13. $100h^2 + 30h + 9$ **14.** $x^2 + 22xy + 121y^2$

_____   _____

15. $25a^2 - 80ab + 64b^2$ **16.** $16u^2 + 56uv + 49v^2$

_____   _____

17. $x^4 + 2x^2 + 1$ **18.** $d^2 + 4cd - 4c^2$

_____   _____

In 19–22, solve.

19. $(x - 2)^2 = 9$ **20.** $(n + 7)^2 = 361$

_____   _____

21. $(3t - 5)^2 = 225$ **22.** $3025 = (9 - d)^2$

_____   _____

NAME _____

LESSON **MASTER** **10−9**
QUESTIONS ON **SPUR** OBJECTIVES

■SKILLS   *Objective B*   *(See pages 527–529 for objectives.)*
In 1–8, multiply and simplify.

1. $(x + 5)(x - 5)$

2. $(2y - 3)(2y + 3)$

3. $(9a + 4b)(9a - 4b)$

4. $(2pr - 7)(2pr + 7)$

5. $(y - \sqrt{10})(y + \sqrt{10})$

6. $\left(a - \dfrac{1}{b}\right)\left(a + \dfrac{1}{b}\right)$

7. $x(3x + 2)(3x - 2)$

8. $2y(y - 6)(y + 6)$

■SKILLS   *Objective E*
In 9–14, write each difference of squares as the product of two binomials.
Otherwise, write "not a difference of squares."

9. $t^2 - 24$

10. $9w^2 - 64$

11. $144b^2 - 25c^2$

12. $z^2 - 0.01$

13. $0.16x^2 - 81$

14. $\frac{4}{9}p^2 - 49q^2$

■PROPERTIES   *Objective F*
In 15–18, show how to calculate mentally by multiplying binomials.

15. $19 \cdot 21$ _____

16. $7.8 \cdot 8.2$ _____

17. $100.1 \cdot 99.9$ _____

18. $6\frac{1}{2} \cdot 7\frac{1}{2}$ _____

LESSON **MASTER** **10–10**
QUESTIONS ON **SPUR** OBJECTIVES

■PROPERTIES   *Objective G (See pages 527–529 for objectives.)*
1. In which of the following can the Zero Product Property be used to solve the equation?

(a) $(x + 5)(x - 1) = 4$ (b) $(3y + 4)(2y - 5) = 9$

(c) $c^2 - 4c = 0$ (d) $t(t - 8)(4t + 6) = 0$ _____

In 2–13, solve.

2. $x(x - 8) = 0$

3. $-3y(2y - 8) = 0$

4. $(L - 7)(4L + 9) = 0$

5. $(2W + 12)(3W + 21) = 0$

6. $0 = (a - 0.4)(a + 0.9)$

7. $(3b - 2.1)(2b + 4.6) = 0$

8. $0 = x(3x + 18)(2x - 9)$

9. $0 = -3a(a + 15)(2a - 7)$

10. $(z - 4)(z + 14)(z + 23) = 0$

11. $0 = (3k + 7)(5k - 8)(4k - 13)$

12. $4x^2 - 8x = 0$

13. $5v^2 = 35v$

■USES   *Objective I*
14. An arrow is shot into the air at 120 feet per second. The distance d above the ground after t seconds is $d = 120t - 16t^2$. After how many seconds will the arrow hit the ground?

15. An arrow is shot up on Mars at 120 feet per second. The distance d above the ground after t seconds is $d = 120t - 6t^2$. After how many seconds will the arrow hit the surface of Mars?

Algebra © Scott, Foresman and Company

LESSON MASTER 10–11
QUESTIONS ON **SPUR** OBJECTIVES

■**PROPERTIES**   *Objective H (See pages 527–529 for objectives.)*
In 1 and 2, answer the question by a. multiplying the binomials, b. testing two special cases.

1. Is $x^2 - 4x + 3$ equal to $(x - 3)(x - 1)$?

a. _____   b. _____

_____

2. Is $2a^2 - 3a - 20$ equal to $(2a + 5)(a - 4)$?

a. _____   b. _____

_____

In 3–8, choose the best answer or write none.

3. $t^2 - 5t - 14 = \underline{\quad ? \quad}$ _____
   (a) $(t + 7)(t - 2)$ (b) $(t - 7)(t + 2)$
   (c) $(t + 7)(t + 2)$ (d) $(t - 7)(t - 2)$

4. $4b^2 + 27b + 18 = \underline{\quad ? \quad}$ _____
   (a) $(2b + 9)(2b + 2)$ (b) $(2b + 6)(2b + 3)$
   (c) $(4b + 3)(b + 6)$ (d) $(4b + 6)(b + 3)$

5. $6x^2 + 5x - 6 = \underline{\quad ? \quad}$ _____
   (a) $(3x + 2)(2x + 3)$ (b) $(3x - 2)(2x - 3)$
   (c) $(3x + 2)(2x - 3)$ (d) $(6x + 1)(x - 6)$

6. $x^2 - 2xy + 3x - 6y = \underline{\quad ? \quad}$ _____
   (a) $(x + 3)(x - 2y)$ (b) $(x - 3)(x + 2y)$
   (c) $(x + 3y)(x - 2)$ (d) $(x - 3y)(x + 2)$

7. $ac - bc + ad - bd = \underline{\quad ? \quad}$ _____
   (a) $(a + b)(c - d)$ (b) $(a + d)(b - c)$
   (c) $(a - d)(b + c)$ (d) $(a - b)(c + d)$

8. $x^3 - x^2 - 6x = \underline{\quad ? \quad}$ _____
   (a) $(x^2 - 3)(x + 2)$ (b) $(x^2 + 2)(x - 3)$
   (c) $x(x - 3)(x + 2)$ (d) $x(x + 3)(x - 2)$

LESSON MASTER 11–1
QUESTIONS ON SPUR OBJECTIVES

■REPRESENTATIONS *Objective H (See pages 583–585 for objectives.)*
In 1–8, solve each system by graphing.

1. $\begin{cases} y = x - 6 \\ y = -2x \end{cases}$ _____

2. $\begin{cases} y = 3x - 9 \\ 6x - 2y = 10 \end{cases}$ _____

3. $\begin{cases} x + y = 5 \\ x - y = 3 \end{cases}$ _____

4. $\begin{cases} 2x + y = 4 \\ 3y = 2x - 12 \end{cases}$ _____

5. $\begin{cases} 2x - 5y = 3 \\ 4y - x = -3 \end{cases}$ _____

6. $\begin{cases} \dfrac{y}{2} = x + 3 \\ y = 2x + 6 \end{cases}$ _____

7. $\begin{cases} 12 = 3x + 2y \\ -10 = x + 2y \end{cases}$ _____

8. $\begin{cases} 7y = 4 - x \\ x = -12 - 7y \end{cases}$ _____

94

LESSON MASTER 11–2
QUESTIONS ON SPUR OBJECTIVES

■SKILLS *Objective A (See pages 583–585 for objectives.)*
In 1–8, solve each system of equations.

1. $\begin{cases} y = 2x - 7 \\ y = 5 - x \end{cases}$

2. $\begin{cases} b = 2a - 1 \\ 2a - 3b = 7 \end{cases}$

3. $\begin{cases} r = 2t \\ 3r - 5t = 2 \end{cases}$

4. $\begin{cases} m = 3n - 5 \\ n + 4m = 6 \end{cases}$

5. $\begin{cases} x = 3n \\ y = 4n \\ 2x + y = 120 \end{cases}$

6. $\begin{cases} x = 5p \\ y = -2p \\ x - 4y = 52 \end{cases}$

7. $\begin{cases} h = 4k \\ 3h + 2k = 21 \end{cases}$

8. $\begin{cases} x = 2 - y \\ x = 5 + 3y \end{cases}$

■USES *Objective F*

9. A boat can travel r mph in still water. This is three times as fast as the current, c, in a river. The boat can go downstream at 12 mph. What is the speed of the boat and the speed of the current?

10. Helen earned $240 in the summer by working at a fast food restaurant and baby-sitting. If she earned five times as much in the restaurant as she did baby-sitting, how much did she earn at each job?

11. In 14-carat gold, there are 14 units of gold for every 10 units of other metal. If a 14-carat gold pendant weighs 0.72 ounces, how much pure gold is in it?

NAME _____

■**SKILLS**   *Objective A (See pages 583–585 for objectives.)*
In 1–8, find the point of intersection of the lines with the given equations.

1. $\begin{cases} y = 3x + 1 \\ y = x - 9 \end{cases}$

2. $\begin{cases} r = 11 - s \\ r = -3s + 9 \end{cases}$

_____   _____

3. $\begin{cases} p = 0.4q + 1.6 \\ p = 0.2q - 1.8 \end{cases}$

4. $\begin{cases} u = 0.6v - 3.2 \\ u = 0.3v - 3.1 \end{cases}$

_____   _____

5. $\begin{cases} y = \frac{1}{2}x - \frac{1}{3} \\ y = \frac{1}{6}x + \frac{1}{4} \end{cases}$

6. $\begin{cases} a = \frac{2}{3}b + \frac{1}{2} \\ a = \frac{1}{6}b + \frac{1}{3} \end{cases}$

_____   _____

■**USES**   *Objective F*

7. A tortoise and a hare are racing. The tortoise goes one foot per second and the hare runs 13 feet per second. The tortoise has a 24 ft head start. (The hare must travel 24 ft more than the tortoise.) How many feet will the hare have to run to catch up with the tortoise?

_____

8. For a certain call one long distance phone company charges $2 for the first three minutes and 60 cents for each additional minute. Another company charges $1.50 for the first three minutes and 70 cents for each additional minute for the same call. After how many minutes beyond three minutes will the total charge be the same for both companies?

_____

NAME _____

LESSON **MASTER** **11-4**
QUESTIONS ON **SPUR** OBJECTIVES

■SKILLS   *Objective B (See pages 583–585 for objectives.)*
In 1–10, solve each system of equations.

1. $\begin{cases} 2x - y = 7 \\ x + y = 5 \end{cases}$

2. $\begin{cases} 3h - k = 7 \\ 2h + k = 8 \end{cases}$

3. $\begin{cases} 3u + 2v = 18 \\ 5u - 2v = 14 \end{cases}$

4. $\begin{cases} 2a + b = 9 \\ 2a - 3b = 5 \end{cases}$

5. $\begin{cases} 2r - 3s = 1 \\ 2r - 4s = 2 \end{cases}$

6. $\begin{cases} 4x - 3y = 30 \\ 7x - 3y = 48 \end{cases}$

7. $\begin{cases} \frac{5}{6}c - d = 2 \\ \frac{2}{3}c + d = 16 \end{cases}$

8. $\begin{cases} \frac{3}{4}a + \frac{1}{3}b = 6 \\ \frac{1}{2}a - \frac{1}{3}b = 4 \end{cases}$

9. $\begin{cases} .04x + .02y = 1.8 \\ .04x - .01y = 1.5 \end{cases}$

10. $\begin{cases} .7y + .2z = 11 \\ .4y - .2z = 11 \end{cases}$

■USES   *Objective F*
11. The sum of two numbers is 79 and their difference is 5. What are the numbers?

12. Three hamburgers and two orders of fries cost $6.10. Four hamburgers and two orders of fries cost $7.60. At these rates, what is the cost h of one hamburger and the cost f of one order of fries?

13. Marianne has two investments. The first pays 4% interest and the second pays 5%. The total annual interest is $130. If the first investment paid 6%, her annual interest would be $170. How much does she have invested at each rate?

Algebra © Scott, Foresman and Company   **97**

LESSON **MASTER** **11–5**
QUESTIONS ON **SPUR** OBJECTIVES

■**SKILLS** *Objective C (See pages 583–585 for objectives.)*
In 1–8, solve each system of equations.

1. $\begin{cases} 5x - 2y = 3 \\ 15x + 8y = 2 \end{cases}$

2. $\begin{cases} 2a + 3b = 2 \\ 6a - 6b = 1 \end{cases}$

3. $\begin{cases} .4x - .2y = 2 \\ .7x + .3y = 23 \end{cases}$

4. $\begin{cases} .05c - .3d = -2.4 \\ .4c + .17d = 6.5 \end{cases}$

5. $\begin{cases} \frac{1}{2}m - \frac{1}{3}n = 8 \\ \frac{3}{4}m + \frac{5}{6}n = 4 \end{cases}$

6. $\begin{cases} \frac{3}{4}c + \frac{2}{3}d = 8 \\ 5c + 2d = 68 \end{cases}$

7. $\begin{cases} 2 = 4h + 7k \\ 1 = 3h + 5k \end{cases}$

8. $\begin{cases} 7r = -6s + 15 \\ -3r + 10s = -1 \end{cases}$

■**USES** *Objective F*

9. The perimeter of a rectangle is 16 cm. If the length is doubled, the perimeter is 26. What are the length and width?

10. A shipping clerk finds that 3 large cartons and 2 small cartons will hold 108 lb. He also finds that 2 large cartons and 3 small cartons hold 102 lb. How much do a large carton and a small carton hold, respectively?

11. For a school play, the eighth graders sold 220 adult tickets and 100 children's tickets. They took in $410 altogether. The ninth graders collected $366 from the sale of 180 adult tickets and 120 children's tickets. What was the price of an adult ticket and a child's ticket?

LESSON **MASTER** **11–6**
QUESTIONS ON **SPUR** OBJECTIVES

■**USES** *Objective G (See pages 583–585 for objectives.)*

1. Two large towns are 60 miles apart. For 20 miles the speed limit is 55 mph. For the rest of the distance the speed limit is 65 mph. If I travel at the speed limit for the entire trip, what will be my average speed?

_____

2. Mark earned the following grades in high school: 6 A's, 7 B's, 4 C's, and 1 D. What is his grade point average? (Assume A = 4, B = 3, C = 2, D = 1.)

_____

3. A final exam consists of two parts: multiple choice questions worth 100 points, and essay questions worth 150 points. Sally got 75 points on the multiple choice section and 95 points on the essay section. What is her average for the whole test?

_____

4. "Slugger" Miller had a batting average of .220 in 120 times at bat on natural grass, and an average of .310 in 180 times at bat on artificial turf. What was his overall batting average?

_____

5. Pure gold is 24 carat. A jeweler mixes 1.2 oz of 14-carat gold with 1.8 oz of 18-carat gold. What is the carat value (purity) of the mixture?

_____

6. A meat manufacturer makes up packages of lunchmeat containing 10 slices of ham worth $.15 each, 8 slices of chicken worth $.12 each and 6 slices of bologna worth $.10 each. How much should he sell the mixture for so as not to lose money?

_____

7. A boat travels 12 miles downstream at 4 mph, and returns upstream the same distance at 3 mph. What is the average speed for the whole trip?

_____

LESSON MASTER 11–7
QUESTIONS ON SPUR OBJECTIVES

■**USES**   *Objective G (See pages 583–585 for objectives.)*

1. At the Math Club bake sale, 20 slices of date-nut bread were sold for 25 cents a slice. There were 10 slices left over. How much should members pay for a leftover slice so that the overall average price per slice is 21 cents?

_____

2. After 8 tests Mario has an average of 78. The final exam is worth 2 tests. The minimum average for a B is 80. What minimum grade does he have to make on the final in order to make a B?

_____

3. Because of heavy traffic a bus averages 20 mph for the first 2 hours of a trip. How long must the bus travel at 60 mph in order to average 40 mph for the entire trip up to that point?

_____

4. In 15 basketball games, Ken has been averaging 18 points a game. How many more games must he play at 25 points per game in order to have an overall average of 20 points per game?

_____

5. How many liters of 60% acid solution must be added to 8 liters of a 40% acid solution to make a mixture that is 50% acid?

_____

6. Harry has $1200 invested at 5%. How much more money must he invest at 8% to have an overall investment of 6%?

_____

7. In a large city, there has been an average of 16 auto accidents a day for 110 days. How many consecutive accident free days must there now be in order to bring the average down to 10 per day?

_____

LESSON MASTER 11−8
QUESTIONS ON **SPUR** OBJECTIVES

■**PROPERTIES**   *Objective E (See pages 583−585 for objectives.)*
In 1−8, a. determine the number of solutions to each system. b. Are the lines parallel?

1. $\begin{cases} 3x - 5y = 9 \\ 12x - 20y = 36 \end{cases}$

   a. _____   b. _____

2. $\begin{cases} 2x + 8y = -20 \\ x - 4y = -10 \end{cases}$

   a. _____   b. _____

3. $\begin{cases} 2a = b + 11 \\ 2a = b - 11 \end{cases}$

   a. _____   b. _____

4. $\begin{cases} 8p = 12 - 2q \\ q + 4p = 6 \end{cases}$

   a. _____   b. _____

5. $\begin{cases} 2(m + 4) = 3(n - 2) \\ 6(m + 1) = 9(n - 4) \end{cases}$

   a. _____   b. _____

6. $\begin{cases} \dfrac{x}{2} + \dfrac{y}{5} = 1 \\ \dfrac{x}{4} + \dfrac{y}{10} = 1 \end{cases}$

   a. _____   b. _____

7. $\begin{cases} 4r = 2(t - 6) \\ 6r = 3(t - 9) \end{cases}$

   a. _____   b. _____

8. $\begin{cases} 2(x - 3) + 3(y - 1) = 6 \\ 3(x - 1) + 2(y - 3) = 6 \end{cases}$

   a. _____   b. _____

■**USES**   *Objective F*
In 9 and 10, could the given situation ever happen?

9. You bought 2 pencils and 1 eraser for 20¢. At the same prices, your friend bought 4 pencils and 2 erasers for 40¢.   _____

10. The mass of 2 pencils and 1 eraser is 40 grams. The mass of 4 pencils and 2 erasers of the same kind is 60 grams.   _____

■**REPRESENTATIONS**   *Objective H*
11. *Multiple choice*   Two straight lines with the same slope and same *y*-intercept intersect in

    (a) exactly one point   (b) exactly two points

    (c) no points   (d) infinitely many points   _____

In 12 and 13, tell whether the statement is true or false.

12. Coincident lines are parallel lines.   _____

13. In a plane, two lines with different slopes must intersect.   _____

LESSON **MASTER** **11–9**
QUESTIONS ON **SPUR** OBJECTIVES

■PROPERTIES   *Objective D* *(See pages 583–585 for objectives.)*
In 1–8, solve.

1. $3t + 1 < 3t + 4$ _____

2. $6(x - 3) = 2(3x + 2)$ _____

3. $8x + 7 > 4(2x + 2)$ _____

4. $-4b + 8b < 4(b + 3)$ _____

5. $5q - 2 = 3q - 2$ _____

6. $12w + 10 = 5(3w + 2)$ _____

7. $2(r - 3) > r - 6$ _____

8. $d + 7 = d - 7$ _____

■USES   *Objective F*

9. Sara deposited $500 in Bank A paying 5% interest. At the same time, she also deposited $500 in Bank B paying 5.5% interest. She withdrew only the interest each year and made no more deposits.
   a. What sentence could you solve to find out when the account in Bank A would have earned more money?

   _____

   b. Solve the sentence to answer the question.   _____

   _____

10. Car rental Company X charges $29.95 a day plus $.15 per mile. Car rental Company Y charges $29.95 a day plus $.20 a mile.
    a. What sentence could you solve to find out after how many miles the charges would be the same?

    _____

    b. Solve the sentence to answer the questions.   _____

    _____

LESSON MASTER 11–10
QUESTIONS ON **SPUR** OBJECTIVES

■**REPRESENTATIONS**   *Objective I (See pages 583–585 for objectives.)*
In 1–6, graph the solution set to each system.

1. $\begin{cases} x + y < 4 \\ x - y > 4 \end{cases}$

2. $\begin{cases} y < x + 3 \\ 2x + y < 3 \end{cases}$

3. $\begin{cases} x > 0 \\ y > 0 \\ x + y < 5 \end{cases}$

4. $\begin{cases} x < 0 \\ y < 0 \\ x + y > \text{-}2 \end{cases}$

5. $\begin{cases} x > 0 \\ y > 0 \\ x < 3 \\ y < 3 \end{cases}$

6. $\begin{cases} x \geq 0 \\ y \geq 0 \\ 2x + y > 1 \\ 2x + y < 4 \end{cases}$

In 7 and 8, write a sentence for and accurately graph the set of points which satisfy each situation.

7. The Drama Club sold tickets for a performance. They sold *s* student tickets and *a* adult tickets. The auditorium holds 80 people. How many adults and students might have bought tickets?

_____

8. The Pep Club has a total of 30 caps and buttons left. They must sell at least 10 caps or buttons to make a profit. If they made a profit, how many caps *c* and buttons *b* might they have sold?

_____

LESSON **MASTER** 12–1
QUESTIONS ON **SPUR** OBJECTIVES

■PROPERTIES *Objective D (See pages 633–635 for objectives.)*

1. What is the shape of the graph of $y = -x^2 + 6x + 8$? _____

In 2–4, tell whether the graph of the equation opens up or down.

2. $y = 3x^2$ _____

3. $y = 9 - x^2$ _____

4. $y = 4 - 2x + x^2$ _____

■REPRESENTATIONS *Objective H*
In 5–8, a. make a table of values and b. graph the equation.

5. $y = 2x^2$

6. $y = -\frac{1}{4}x^2$

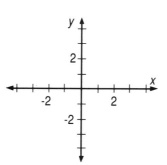

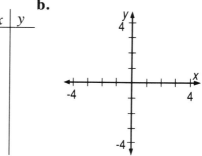

7. $y = -x^2 + 3$

8. $y = x^2 - x - 6$

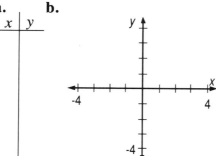

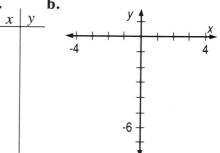

9. *Multiple choice* Which could be the graph of $y = x^2 + 2x + 1$? _____

(a)

(b)

(c)

(d)

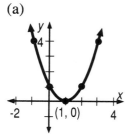
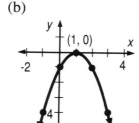
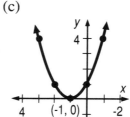
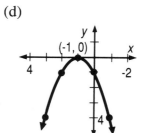

Algebra © Scott, Foresman and Company

LESSON MASTER 12-2
QUESTIONS ON **SPUR** OBJECTIVES

■**REPRESENTATIONS**   *Objective H (See pages 633–635 for objectives.)*
In 1–4, put the equation in a form in which it can be graphed with an automatic grapher.

1. $2x + y = 6$ _____

2. $6x + 2y = x^2$ _____

3. $x^2 + y - 3x = 0$ _____

4. $3x^2 - 6x - 2y = 0$ _____

In 5–8, give a suitable window that will give a graph that includes the vertex.

5. $y = 2x^2 + x - 1$ _____

6. $y = x^2 - 6x + 8$ _____

7. $y = x^2 - 3x + 16$ _____

8. $y = 9x - x^2$ _____

In 9 and 10, graph the equation and estimate the vertex.

9. $y = 3x^2 + 6x - 1$ _____   **10.** $y = 2x^2 - 8x + 3$ _____

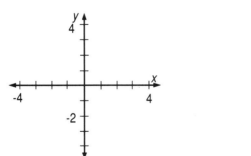   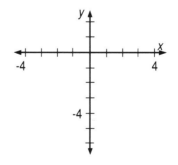

In 11 and 12, describe the window.

11. _____   **12.** _____

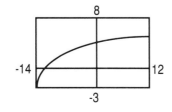   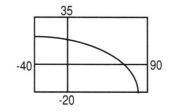

LESSON **MASTER** **12–3**
QUESTIONS ON **SPUR** OBJECTIVES

■USES *Objective G (See pages 633–635 for objectives.)*

1. A baseball crosses home plate at a height of 4 ft. The batter hits the ball into the air. The path of the ball is described by the equation below where h is the height of the ball in feet and x is the number of feet the ball is downfield.

$$h = -\frac{1}{729}(x - 162)^2 + 40.$$

The outfield wall is 6 ft high and 318 ft from home plate. Will the ball go over the wall for a home run? If so, by how many feet will it clear the wall?

_____ _____

2. Suppose the outfield wall in Question 1 was 324 feet from home plate. Would it be possible for an outfielder to catch the ball? If so, at what height above the ground would the ball be when he caught it with his back against the wall?

_____ _____

3. A ball is thrown upward from the surface of Mars with an initial velocity of 36 feet per second. Its approximate height h above the surface after a time of t seconds is given by the equation: $h = 36t - 6t^2$.

a. What is its height after 2 seconds? _____

b. What is its height after 6 seconds? _____

c. From the answer in part **b.**, after how many seconds will it reach its highest point, and how high will it be? _____ _____

4. Refer to the graph at the right. It shows the height of a ball at a time of t seconds after it is thrown upward with an initial velocity of 30 meters per second.

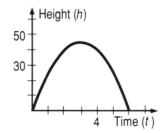

a. Estimate from the graph its height h after 1 second.

_____

b. Estimate from the graph when it will reach a height of 30 meters. _____

c. What is the maximum height? _____

Algebra © Scott, Foresman and Company

LESSON MASTER 12–4
QUESTIONS ON SPUR OBJECTIVES

■SKILLS   *Objective A (See pages 633–635 for objectives.)*
In 1–6, give the exact solutions to the equation.

1. $3x^2 - 10x + 8 = 0$ **2.** $14a^2 + 13a + 3 = 0$

_____   _____

3. $t^2 - 10t = -25$ **4.** $(n + 2)(n - 4) = 7$

_____   _____

5. $4r - r^2 = -21$ **6.** $10p - p^2 = 24$

_____   _____

In 7 and 8, a. find a simpler equation that has the same solution. b. Then solve the equation.

7. $3x^2 - 27x + 54 = 0$ **8.** $16y^2 + 28y - 8 = 0$

a. _____   a. _____

b. _____   b. _____

In 9 and 10, solve. Approximate solutions to the nearest tenth.

9. $x^2 + 3x - 5 = 0$ **10.** $(2c - 1)(c + 2) = 5$

_____   _____

■PROPERTIES   *Objective E*
In 11 and 12, tell whether the statement is true or false.

11. Some quadratic equations cannot be solved using
the Quadratic Formula.   _____

12. To apply the Quadratic Formula, one side of a
quadratic equation must be zero.   _____

■USES   *Objective G*

13. The height h in feet of a ball thrown upward on Mars after a time of t
seconds is given by $h = 48t - 6t^2$. At what times was the ball 30 feet
above the surface?

_____

14. The side of a square is n cm. If the length is increased by 5 cm and the
width is decreased by 4 cm, the resulting rectangle has an area of
112 square cm. What was the length of the side of the square?

_____

LESSON **MASTER** **12–5**
QUESTIONS ON **SPUR** OBJECTIVES

■SKILLS *Objective A (See pages 633–635 for objectives.)*
In 1 and 2, give the exact solutions to the equation.

1. $2x^2 + 13x - 7 = 0$

2. $x^2 - 7x - 3 = 0$

_____

_____

■PROPERTIES *Objective D*
In 3–6, tell how many times the graph of the equation intersects the *x*-axis.

3. $y = 2x^2 - 5x - 7$

4. $y = 7x^2 + 6x + 2$

_____

_____

5. $y = 4x^2 - 4x + 1$

6. $y = x^2 - 9x - 22$

_____

_____

■PROPERTIES *Objective E*
**In 7–9, let *D* be the discriminant of the equation $ax^2 + bx + c = 0$.
Match the answers.**

7. $D > 0$ _____

(a) no real solutions

8. $D = 0$ _____

(b) two real solutions

9. $D < 0$ _____

(c) one real solution

**In 10–15, a. find the value of the discriminant, and b. determine the
number of real solutions to the equation.**

10. $5x^2 - x + 2 = 0$

11. $a^2 - 6a = 8$

a. _____ b. _____

a. _____ b. _____

12. $1 + 6n + 9n^2 = 0$

13. $0.6k^2 - 1.39k + 2 = 0$

a. _____ b. _____

a. _____ b. _____

14. $1.1p^2 + 3.2p - 1.2 = 0$

15. $\frac{1}{4}x^2 + \frac{1}{2}x + \frac{1}{3} = 0$

a. _____ b. _____

a. _____ b. _____

LESSON **MASTER** 12–6
QUESTIONS ON **SPUR** OBJECTIVES

■**PROPERTIES**   *Objective E (See pages 633–635 for objectives.)*

1. *Multiple choice*   If its discriminant is a nonzero perfect square, a quadratic equation has:

   (a) one real solution   (b) two irrational solutions

   (c) two rational solutions   (d) none of these   _____

**In 2–7, a. use the discriminant to determine the number of real solutions.
b. Tell whether the real solutions are rational or irrational.**

2. $x^2 - 8x + 3 = 0$ **3.** $16a^2 + 8a + 1 = 0$

   a. _____   **a.** _____

   b. _____   **b.** _____

4. $13y^2 - 4 = 0$ **5.** $t(t + 2) = 4$

   a. _____   **a.** _____

   b. _____   **b.** _____

6. $4b(b + 2) = 5$ **7.** $9r^2 + 16 = 0$

   a. _____   **a.** _____

   b. _____   **b.** _____

■**PROPERTIES**   *Objective F*
In 8–13, tell whether the number is rational or irrational.

8. $\sqrt{32}$ _____   **9.** 19.031 _____

10. $-\dfrac{2}{3}$ _____   **11.** $\dfrac{3\pi}{2}$ _____

12. $\sqrt{144}$ _____   **13.** $6.\overline{4}$ _____

LESSON **MASTER** **12-7**
QUESTIONS ON **SPUR** OBJECTIVES

■SKILLS *Objective B (See pages 633-635 for objectives.)*
In 1-12, a. use the discriminant to determine which quadratic trinomials are factorable. b. If possible, factor.

1. $t^2 + t - 12$

_____

2. $r^2 + 16r + 15$

_____

3. $3x^2 - 7x + 4$

_____

4. $n^2 - 7n - 18$

_____

5. $y^2 + 9y + 20$

_____

6. $24a^2 + 10a - 21$

_____

7. $12c^2 + 7c - 45$

_____

8. $3x^2 - 10x + 3$

_____

9. $2x^2 - x - 10$

_____

10. $5x^2 - 14 - 3x$

_____

11. $6 - 25t + 4t^2$

_____

12. $6y^2 - 4y - 3$

_____

In 13-18, a. factor the trinomial into the product of a monomial and a trinomial. b. Complete the factoring by finding the factors of the trinomial.

13. $x^3 - 3x^2 + 2x$

a. _____

b. _____

14. $y^3 + 8y^2 + 12y$

a. _____

b. _____

15. $2a^3 - 6a^2 - 8a$

a. _____

b. _____

16. $r^4 + 8r^3 + 12r^2$

a. _____

b. _____

17. $3t^3 - 12t^2 + 12t$

a. _____

b. _____

18. $5a^4 + 10a^3 + 5a^2$

a. _____

b. _____

Algebra © Scott, Foresman and Company

LESSON **MASTER** 12–8
QUESTIONS ON **SPUR** OBJECTIVES

■SKILLS *Objective C (See pages 633–635 for objectives.)*
In 1–14, solve by factoring.

1. $x^2 + 14x + 24 = 0$

2. $a^2 - 4a - 21 = 0$

_____

3. $2y^2 + 5y - 3 = 0$

4. $2r^2 - 17r + 21 = 0$

_____

5. $c^2 - 16 = 0$

6. $k^2 - 64 = 0$

_____

7. $4t^2 + 15t = 4$

8. $6x^2 = x + 35$

_____

9. $y^3 + 9y^2 + 20y = 0$

10. $(n - 2)(n + 3) = 6$

_____

11. $(b + 1)(b + 5) = 45$

12. $4d^3 + 11d^2 - 3d = 0$

_____

13. $p^2 - 8p = 0$

14. $a^3 - 9a^2 = 0$

_____

■USES *Objective G*

15. In a round-robin tournament, 66 games were played. The expression
$$\frac{n^2 - n}{2}$$
gives the number of games played in the tournament for n teams. How many teams were in the tournament?

_____

16. One formula for finding the approximate stopping distance d (in feet) of an automobile going x mph on a wet road is
$$d = \frac{10x + x^2}{10}.$$
If it took 20 ft to stop a car, how fast was it going?

_____

LESSON MASTER 12–9
QUESTIONS ON SPUR OBJECTIVES

■SKILLS   *Objective B (See pages 633–635 for objectives.)*
In 1–4, given that *p* and *q* are solutions to the quadratic equation, write the factors of the quadratic expression.

1. $x^2 - 11x - 42 = 0$; $p = 14$, $q = $ -3   _____

2. $y^2 - 28y + 96 = 0$; $p = 4$, $q = 24$ _____

3. $2a^2 - a - 36 = 0$; $p = $ -4, $q = \frac{9}{2}$ _____

4. $3c^2 + 22c + 24 = 0$; $p = $ -6, $q = -\frac{4}{3}$ _____

In 5–8, a quadratic equation is given with one of its solutions. Use this information to factor.

5. $x^2 - 39x + 108 = 0$; 3   6. $t^2 - 48t + 540 = 0$; 18

_____   _____

7. $4a^2 - 11a - 45 = 0$; $-\frac{9}{4}$ 8. $12x^2 - 43x + 36 = 0$; $\frac{4}{3}$

_____   _____

In 9–11, factor the expression as much as possible.

9. $2y^3 - 3y + y^2$ _____

10. $15x^3 + 41x^2 + 14x$ _____

11. $c^4 - 36c^3 + 320c^2$ _____

Algebra © Scott, Foresman and Company

NAME _____

LESSON MASTER 13-1
QUESTIONS ON **SPUR** OBJECTIVES

■PROPERTIES *Objective C* *(See pages 673–675 for objectives.)*
In 1–6, tell whether or not the equation determines a function.

1. $x = 2y + 5$ _____   2. $y = |2x - 5|$ _____

3. $x^2 = y - 4$ _____   4. $x = |y - 3|$ _____

5. $y^2 = x$ _____   6. $y = 100(1.06)^x$ _____

In 7–10, tell whether or not the set of ordered pairs is a function.

7. $\{(1, 3), (2, 4), (3, 5)\}$ _____   8. $\{(2, 5), (3, 5), (4, 5)\}$ _____

9. $\{(\pi, 5), (\pi, 4), (0, 0)\}$ _____   10. $\{(a, b), (b, c), (c, d)\}$ _____

■PROPERTIES *Objective D*
**In 11–14, classify the function as (a) linear, (b) quadratic, or
(c) exponential.**

11. $y = x(x + 2)$ _____   12. $y = 2^2 - x$ _____

13. $y = 2^x$ _____   14. $y = x^2$ _____

■REPRESENTATIONS *Objective H*
**In 15–20, tell whether or not the set of ordered pairs graphed is a
function.**

15. _____   16. _____   17. _____

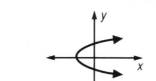   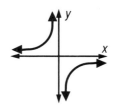

18. _____   19. _____   20. _____

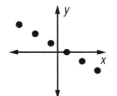   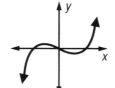   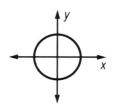

21. *True or False* Any vertical line passing through the graph of
a function will intersect the graph in no more than one point. _____

Algebra © Scott, Foresman and Company   **113**

LESSON **MASTER 13-2**
QUESTIONS ON **SPUR** OBJECTIVES

■SKILLS *Objective A (See pages 673–675 for objectives.)*
In 1–6, $f(x) = x^2 - 8x + 12$. **Calculate.**

1. $f(2)$ _____

2. $f(-1)$ _____

3. $f(0)$ _____

4. $f(6)$ _____

5. $f(1.5)$ _____

6. $f(-\frac{9}{2})$ _____

7. If $s(n) = \sqrt{n - 8}$, what is $s(12)$? _____

8. If $g(x) = 2^x - 1$, find $g(2) + g(3)$. _____

9. If $A(t) = -2t + 3$, calculate $\dfrac{A(5) - A(2)}{3}$. _____

10. If $A(r) = \pi r^2$, find $A(2)$. _____

■REPRESENTATIONS *Objective I*
In 11–14, **graph each function.**

11. $f(x) = 2(x - 1)$

12. $g(x) = 1 - x^2$

13. $h(t) = \left(\frac{1}{2}\right)^t$

14. $k(n) = 5$, n an integer between -2 and 2.

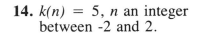

114

LESSON MASTER 13-3
QUESTIONS ON **SPUR** OBJECTIVES

■SKILLS   *Objective A (See pages 673–675 for objectives.)*
In 1–6, $f(x) = |24 - x|$. Calculate.

1. $f(36)$ _____

2. $f(0)$ _____

3. $f(-6)$ _____

4. $10 - f(28)$ _____

5. $f(20.5) + f(22.5)$ _____

6. $f(-3.5) - f(-1.5)$ _____

In 7 and 8, $g(t) = -150|t - 4| + 800$. Calculate.

7. $g(8)$ _____

8. $g(5.5) - g(4.5)$ _____

■PROPERTIES   *Objective D*
In 9–12, classify the function as (a) linear, (b) quadratic, or (c) absolute value.

9. $f(x) = 3x^2 + 2x$ _____

10. $y = |\frac{1}{2}x + 5|$ _____

11. $g(x) = -\frac{2}{3}x + |-7|$ _____

12. $y = |-\frac{2}{3}x| - 7$ _____

■REPRESENTATIONS   *Objective I*
In 13–16, graph each function.

13. $g(x) = |6 - x|$

14. $h(t) = |t| + 4$

15. $A(r) = |2r|$, when r is between -3 and 3.

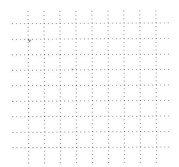

16. $V(t) = -|t|$, when t is an integer between -3 and 3.

LESSON MASTER 13–4
QUESTIONS ON SPUR OBJECTIVES

■**PROPERTIES**   *Objective E (See pages 673–675 for objectives.)*

1. What number cannot be in the domain of $f(x) = \dfrac{2}{x - 1}$? _____

In 2–5, give the domain for each function.

2. $f(x) = -7x + 9$ _____

3. $A(t) = t^2 - 4$ _____

4. $g(x) = \sqrt{x}$ _____

5. $C(n) = 4.5n$, where n is the
   number of books bought. _____

In 6–9, give the domain and range.

	Domain	**Range**
6. $f(x) = 2x + 5$	_____	_____
7. $g(x) = \|3x + 10\|$	_____	_____
8. $h(t) = \sqrt{t} + 5$	_____	_____
9. $\{(1, 5), (2, 8), (3, 5)\}$	_____	_____

10. *Multiple choice*   The domain of a function is $\{1, 2, 3\}$. The range is
$\{2, 4, 6\}$. Which of these could be the rule for the function?

(a) $y = x + 2$ (b) $y = 2x$ (c) $y = .5x$ (d) $y = 2|x|$ _____

**In 11 and 12, give a. the domain and b. the range of each function
graphed below.**

11. a. domain _____   **12. a. domain** _____

  b. range _____   **b. range** _____

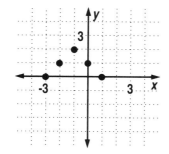   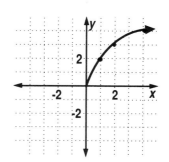

LESSON **MASTER 13–5**
QUESTIONS ON **SPUR** OBJECTIVES

■**USES** *Objective F (See pages 673–675 for objectives.)*
In 1–4, use the spinner to determine the probabilities.

1. P*(A)* _____

2. P*(B)* _____

3. P*(C)* _____

4. P*(D)* _____

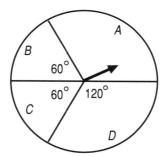

In 5–9, two dice in the shape of a triangular base pyramid are tossed. The faces are numbered 1 to 4, and are equally likely to appear.

5. P(sum is 2) _____

6. P(sum is 4) _____

7. P(sum is 7) _____

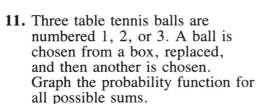

8. P(sum is even) _____

9. The batting average of a baseball player is an indication of the probability that the player will get a hit in a time at bat. In 1987, Tony Gwynn of San Diego had a batting average of .369. What was the probability that he would not get a hit in a time at bat?

_____

■**REPRESENTATIONS** *Objective I*

10. Graph the probability function for the numbers on the spinner.

11. Three table tennis balls are numbered 1, 2, or 3. A ball is chosen from a box, replaced, and then another is chosen. Graph the probability function for all possible sums.

LESSON MASTER 13–6
QUESTIONS ON SPUR OBJECTIVES

■**SKILLS** *Objective B (See pages 673–675 for objectives.)*
In 1–6, use a calculator to find each of the values to the nearest thousandth.

1. tan 22.5° _____   **2.** tan 72.6° _____   **3.** tan 62.7° _____

4. tan 7.1° _____   **5.** (tan 60°)² _____   **6.** $\dfrac{1}{\tan 45°}$ _____

In 7–10, find the measure of each angle to the nearest tenth of a degree.

7. m∠A if tan A = 1.036 _____   **8.** m∠B if tan A = .556 _____

9. m∠C if tan A = .048 _____   **10.** m∠D if tan A = 3.549 _____

In 11–14, use the picture.

11. tan A = _____   **12.** m∠A = _____

13. tan B = _____   **14.** m∠B = _____

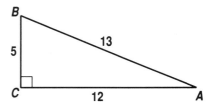

■**USES** *Objective G*

15. Sara looks up at an angle of 35° to the top of the Gateway Arch in St. Louis from a viewing point 900 feet from the base of the Arch. Approximately how tall is the Arch if Sara's eyes are 5 feet above the ground?

_____

16. Ben's eyes are 170 cm above the ground. When he stands 20 m from the base of a fire tower, he has to look up at an angle of 40° to see the top. How high is the tower?

_____

17. What angle does the upper half of the line y = -0.6x + 2 make with the positive ray of the x-axis?

_____

18. What is the slope of a line which makes an angle of 68° with the positive ray of the x-axis?

_____

118   *Algebra* © Scott, Foresman and Company

LESSON **MASTER** **13–7**
QUESTIONS ON **SPUR** OBJECTIVES

■SKILLS   *Objective B (See pages 673–675 for objectives.)*
In 1–14, approximate to the nearest thousandth.

1. $\sqrt{21,443}$ _____

2. 11! _____

3. $\frac{1}{13}$ _____

4. SQR(11.4) _____

5. tan 48° _____

6. sin 26.5° _____

7. log 1000 _____

8. cos 143° _____

9. $(2.63)^{-2}$ _____

10. tan (-25°) _____

11. 3! · 4! _____

12. sin 1285° _____

13. $\sqrt{0.0256}$ _____

14. log 0.789 _____

Multiple choice   **In 15–19, tell which number is not in the domain of the given function.**

15. SQR   (a) 0.5   (b) -4   (c) $(3)^{-2}$ (d) 0   _____

16. LOG   (a) 0.5   (b) -4   (c) $\frac{1}{3}$ (d) 1600   _____

17. tan   (a) 0.5°   (b) -4°   (c) 1000°   (d) 90°   _____

18. FACT   (a) 0.5   (b) 2140   (c) 3^2 (d) 0   _____

19. $\frac{1}{x}$ (a) 0.5   (b) -4   (c) $(3)^2$ (d) 0   _____

Answers

LESSON MASTER 1–1
QUESTIONS ON **SPUR** OBJECTIVES

■SKILLS *Objective A* *(See pages 50–53 for objectives.)*
In 1–4, convert the fractions to decimals and write an inequality to compare them.

1. $\frac{5}{8}, \frac{2}{3}$ $.625 < .\overline{6}$ 2. $\frac{5}{12}, \frac{7}{16}$ $.41\overline{6} < .4375$

3. $\frac{13}{20}, \frac{5}{8}$ $.65 > .625$ 4. $\frac{27}{41}, \frac{31}{45}$ $.65853 < .68\overline{8}$

■SKILLS *Objective B*
In 5 and 6, use trial and error to find which of the given numbers are solutions to the open sentences.

5. $4x + 3 = 15$ 1, 3, 5   ____3____

6. $5x + 9 = 7x + 1$ 4, 5, 6   ____4____

In 7 and 8, find three solutions to each inequality.

7. $4x - 2 > 11$ sample: 4, 5, 6 $(x > \frac{13}{4})$

8. $x + 11 \geq 2x + 7$ sample: 1, 2, 3 $(x \leq 4)$

■REPRESENTATIONS *Objective K*
In 9–12, write an inequality to describe each graph. Use the variable that is next to the graph.

9.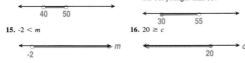
____$x > 4$____

10.
____$y \leq 30$____

11.
____$8 < p < 20$____

12.
____$40 \leq y < 80$____

In 13–16, graph the inequality given or suggested by the situation.

13. I weigh between 40 kg and 50 kg.
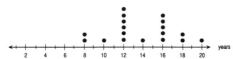

14. Our teacher is at least 30 years old but younger than 55.

15. $-2 < m$
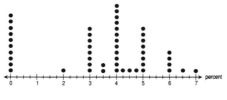

16. $20 \geq c$

Algebra © Scott, Foresman and Company   **1**

LESSON MASTER 1–2
QUESTIONS ON **SPUR** OBJECTIVES

■USES *Objective H* *(See pages 50–53 for objectives.)*
1. a. A sample group of students was asked how much allowance each received during the week. They received $5, $4, $5, $7, $5, $4, $6, $3, $5, $5. Find the mean, median, and mode.

Mean: __$4.89__ Median: __$5__ Mode: __$5__

b. *True or false* There are as many amounts greater than or equal to the mean as there are less than or equal to the mean.   ____false____

2. In ten games played, the points scored by the football team were 21, 14, 15, 3, 10, 15, 28, 20, 12, 10. Find the mean, median, and mode.

Mean: __14.8__ Median: __14.5__ Mode: __10, 15__

3. *True or false* The mean is always larger than the median.   ____false____

4. Give a set of data which has two modes.   sample: 1, 2, 2, 3, 3, 4, 5

5. Give a set of data in which the mean and the median are the same.   sample: 1, 2, 3, 4, 5

In 6–8, which measure of central tendency (mean, median, mode) do you think is the best statistic to use to find the answer?

6. Jay did 90, 100, 100, 100, 100, and 100 sit-ups in six workouts. How many sit-ups does Jay usually do in each workout?   ____mode____

7. Caryl received quiz scores of 0, 90, 94, 96, and 100. What is her "average" score?   ____mean____

8. Six students earned $2, $2, $4, $4, $6, and $6 weeding flower beds. What is the "average" payment for this job?   median/mean

■REPRESENTATIONS *Objective L*
9. Russ worked twelve days at his part-time job in February, with his time card showing the following hours: 1.5, 4, 2.5, 5, 3, 3.5, 2.5, 6, 2.5, 2, 2, and 4.5. Draw a dot frequency diagram for this data.

2 *Continued*   *Algebra © Scott, Foresman and Company*

LESSON MASTER 1–2
(page 2)

10. Find the mean, median, and mode for the data given in the previous question.

Mean: __3.25__ Median: __2.75__ Mode: __2.5__

11. Parents of a group of students reported the years of schooling they had (excluding kindergarten). The dot frequency diagram shows their responses.

a. Find the mean, median, and mode.

Mean: __13.78__ Median: __13__ Mode: __12__

b. *True or false* Half of the parents had some schooling beyond high school.   ____true____

12. Below are the state sales tax rates charged on restaurant meals in the 50 states.

a. How many states charge 4% or less?   ____33____

b. How many states use tax rates that involve a fraction of a percent?   ____6____

c. Find the mode for the data.   ____4____

d. Find the mean for the data.   ____3.44____

Algebra © Scott, Foresman and Company   **3**

LESSON MASTER 1–3
QUESTIONS ON **SPUR** OBJECTIVES

■REPRESENTATIONS *Objective K* *(See pages 50–53 for objectives.)*
1. An automobile manufacturer advertises that its car will get from 28 to 35 miles per gallon depending on the speed at which the car is driven.

a. Express this interval as an inequality using *m* for mileage.
$28 \leq m \leq 35$

b. Graph the inequality.
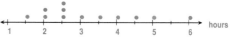

2. Graph the closed interval 16 ± 0.5.
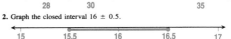

In 3–6, graph the inequality.

3. $2 \leq x < 8$

4. $25 > y > 15$

5. $\{n \leq 5$ where n is a whole number$\}$

6. $\{p < 12$ where p is a whole number$\}$

7. Graph the open interval from 20 to 50.

8. An interval has a range of 8 and midpoint 5. Graph the interval.

In 9 and 10, find the range of the interval.

9. 36 ± 8 ____16____   10. 4 ± 1.2 ____2.4____

11. The number of *A*'s given by a group of algebra teachers varied from 2 to 9. Draw a graph showing this interval.

4   *Algebra © Scott, Foresman and Company*

LESSON MASTER 1–4
QUESTIONS ON **SPUR** OBJECTIVES

■**SKILLS** *Objective C (See pages 50–53 for objectives.)*
In 1–3, evaluate the numerical expressions.

1. $12 + 2 * 4$ — 20

2. $16 - \frac{8}{2} + 6$ — 18

3. $\frac{3 + 7}{2} + 3$ — 8

4. *True or false* $3x^2 = (3x)^2$ — false

5. Find the value of $3(m + n)$ when $m = 1.2$ and $n = 2.6$ — 11.4

6. Evaluate $\frac{r + s}{r - s}$ when $r = 5$ and $s = 3$. — 4

7. Evaluate $9b^2$ when $b = \frac{1}{3}$. — 1

8. Evaluate $\left(\frac{3n}{4}\right)^2$ when $n = 2$. — $\frac{9}{4}$

■**SKILLS** *Objective D*
9. If the program below is run, and 1.6 is the input, what will be printed?

```
10  PRINT "EVALUATE AN EXPRESSION"
20  PRINT "ENTER A NUMBER"
30  INPUT X
40  PRINT 6 + 32/X − 10
50  END
```

EVALUATE AN EXPRESSION

ENTER A NUMBER, 16

10. The formula for changing Celsius temperature to Fahrenheit is:
$$F = \frac{9}{5}C + 32$$

a. Write a computer program which will find F for an input of any C.

```
sample: 10  PRINT "FIND FAHRENHEIT FROM CELSIUS"
        20  PRINT "ENTER A CELSIUS TEMPERATURE"
        30  INPUT C
        40  PRINT 9/5 * C + 32
        50  END
```

b. What is the Fahrenheit temperature when $C = 28$? — 82.4

LESSON MASTER 1–5
QUESTIONS ON **SPUR** OBJECTIVES

■**SKILLS** *Objective D (See pages 50–53 for objectives.)*
1. When the program below is run, what will be printed if 3 is input?

```
10  PRINT "ENTER A NUMBER"
20  INPUT N
30  LET D = (N − 1) * (N + 1) + 2
40  PRINT N, D
50  END
```

ENTER A NUMBER; 3, 10

■**USES** *Objective I*
2. In a league with n teams, each team plays every other team twice (home and away). The total number of games played is $n(n − 1)$. How many games are played in an 8-team league? — 56

3. The distance, in feet, required to stop a car going s miles per hour is about
$$s + \frac{s^2}{20}.$$
How many feet will a car going 60 mph take to stop? — 240

4. The lateral area (where the label is placed) of a can of beans is $2\pi rh$, where r is the radius of the bottom, and h the height of the can. Find the lateral area if the radius is 5 cm and the height 14 cm. — 140π cm²

5. In some schools, the grade point average is given by:
$$\frac{4a + 3b + 2c + d}{a + b + c + d + f}.$$
where a is the number of A's, b is the number of B's, c is the number of C's, d is the number of D's, and f is the number of F's. Carol had 2 A's, 2 B's and a D on her report card. Find her grade point average. — 3

6. Threshold weight is the maximum weight for a person in good health. For men aged 40–49, the threshold weight in pounds is given by
$$\left(\frac{h}{12.3}\right)^3 \quad h \text{ is height in inches}$$
What is the threshold weight for a 45-year-old man 67 in. tall? — ≈162 lb

---

LESSON MASTER 1–6
QUESTIONS ON **SPUR** OBJECTIVES

■**PROPERTIES** *Objective E (See pages 50–53 for objectives.)*
In 1–3, use the set $\{3, 1.2, -4, 0, \sqrt{3}\}$.

1. Which elements are whole numbers? — 3 and 0

2. Which elements are integers? — 3, -4, and 0

3. Which elements are real numbers? — 3, 1.2, -4, 0, and $\sqrt{3}$

In 4–6, let S be the solution set. Find $N(S)$.

4. $4 < x \le 8$ where the domain is W, the set of whole numbers. — 4

5. $n^2 = 4$ where the domain is I. — 2

6. $x + 2 = 5$ where the domain is R. — 1

7. If S = the set of states of the U.S. and R = the set of U.S. Senators, compare $N(S)$ and $N(R)$.

$N(R) = 2N(S)$ or $N(R) > N(S)$

8. *True or false* The set of living dinosaurs = ø. — true

■**USES** *Objective G*
In 9–12, a set is given. State whether the set is discrete or continuous and give a sample element of the set.

9. the set of tonight's TV programs — discrete; M*A*S*H

10. the set of distances from school — continuous; $\frac{1}{3}$ mile

11. the set of all integers — discrete; 1

12. the set of fractions between 0 and 1 — continuous; $\frac{1}{2}$

In 13–15, choose a domain for the variable from these:
real numbers   whole numbers   positive real numbers   integers

13. n, the number of cars in a parking lot. — whole numbers

14. t, the time it takes to walk to school. — positive real numbers

15. m, the number of months the rainfall in Seattle was greater than 1 inch. — whole numbers

---

LESSON MASTER 1–7
QUESTIONS ON **SPUR** OBJECTIVES

■**PROPERTIES** *Objective F (See pages 50–53 for objectives.)*
1. A number is selected randomly from the set of integers between 1 and 50 inclusive. What is the probability that it is divisible by 7? — $\frac{7}{50}$

2. Marie is in a class of 30 students. Five are to be picked at random for a committee. What is the probability that she will be picked? — $\frac{1}{6}$

3. A hexagonal pencil (six faces) has printing on one face. When it is rolled, what is the probability that the printed face will not come up? — $\frac{5}{6}$

4. In a "Pick Three" lottery you pick any three digits. If they come up in the same order as you picked them, you win. If you picked 587, what is the probability you will win? — $\frac{1}{1000}$

5. Two fair dice are thrown. Find the probability of each of the following.

   a. Sum is 8. — $\frac{5}{36}$

   b. Sum is not 2 or 12. — $\frac{17}{18}$

   c. Sum is greater than 7. — $\frac{5}{12}$

6. Jack is in a race with three other boys with about his speed. He says, "Either I will win or I won't. So the probability I will win is $\frac{1}{2}$." What is wrong with his argument?
Winning and losing are not equally likely.

7. A card is picked randomly from a standard deck of 52 playing cards. What is the probability that it is a heart? — $\frac{1}{4}$

8. If an event has the probability of .75 of happening, what is the probability that it won't happen? — .25

9. Which is more likely to happen: throwing a 2 with a die, or throwing a head with a fair coin? — throwing a head

10. A letter is picked at random from the letters in the word *Mississippi*. What is the probability that it is an *s*? — $\frac{4}{11}$

LESSON MASTER 1–8
QUESTIONS ON **SPUR** OBJECTIVES

■SKILLS *Objective A* (See pages 50–53 for objectives.)
In 1–6, simplify using the Equal Fractions Property.

1. $\frac{42}{315}$ $\frac{2}{15}$ 2. $\frac{4a}{9ab}$ $\frac{4}{9b}$

3. $\frac{4\pi r^2}{2\pi r}$ $2r$ 4. $\frac{11abc}{44a}$ $\frac{bc}{4}$

5. $\frac{2(x+y)}{4(x+y)}$ $\frac{1}{2}$ 6. $\frac{35rs^3}{21rs^2}$ $\frac{5s}{3}$

7. *True or false* By the Equal Fractions
Property, $\frac{x+3}{x+6} = \frac{1}{2}$.   **false**

8. What is x if $\frac{3x}{25} = \frac{24}{100}$?   **2**

■USES *Objective J*

9. In a presidential preference poll, 52% preferred candidate A, 44% preferred candidate B, and 4% were undecided. Give two possibilities for the number of people polled, and how many were in each group.

samples: 100 people polled, 52 for A, 44 for B, 4 undecided; 200 people polled, 104 for A, 88 for B, 8 undecided.

10. In 1982 there were 26 physicians for every 100,000 people in India. If the population of India was 713 million, about how many physicians were there in India?

185,380

11. A 1982 Nielsen poll showed 50,150,000 American households out of 83,300,000 watched the final episode of M*A*S*H. What was the relative frequency of a household watching the program?

$\frac{50,150,000}{83,300,000} = \frac{59}{98}$, or about .6

12. An event occurs n times out of 100 possibilities. What is its relative frequency?

$\frac{n}{100}$

LESSON MASTER 2–1
QUESTIONS ON **SPUR** OBJECTIVES

■PROPERTIES *Objective E* (See pages 102–105 for objectives.)
In 1–6, identify what property of addition is given.

1. $3 + -2 = -2 + 3$ **Commutative**

2. $(a + 4) + 6 = a + (4 + 6)$ **Associative**

3. $(x + 3) + 2 = 2 + (x + 3)$ **Commutative**

4. $4 + (6 + -2) = 4 + (-2 + 6)$ **Commutative**

5. $3 + (-2 + a) = (3 + -2) + a$ **Associative**

6. $m + (b + -3) + 3 = m + b + (-3 + 3)$ **Associative**

In 7–10, use the associative and commutative properties to add mentally.

7. $9 + -3 + 2 + -6$ **2**   8. $3.2 + -0.6 + -0.2 + 4.6$ **7**

9. $998 + 200 + 2 + 50$ **1250**   10. $\frac{3}{5} + \frac{-1}{3} + \frac{2}{5}$ $\frac{2}{3}$

■USES *Objective H*
11. For the first four months of the year (January–April), the profits of Patty's Pizza Co. were $540, $120, $460, and $180. Mentally find the total for this period.

$1300

12. In a game show, Frank won $100 on the first question and n dollars on the second but lost q dollars on the third. He ended up with $300. Write a sentence relating these quantities.

$100 + n - q = 300$

13. Before a summer storm, the temperature was 86°. It then fell $d°$ and later rose 5°. The new temperature was less than 80°. Write a sentence for the final temperature and simplify.

$86 - d + 5 < 80,\ 11 < d$

14. Write an expression for the perimeter of this triangle.

$(x - 1) + (x + 8) + 37$

LESSON MASTER 2–2
QUESTIONS ON **SPUR** OBJECTIVES

■SKILLS *Objective B* (See pages 102–105 for objectives.)
In 1–8, simplify.

1. $-3 + t + -8$ $t - 11$ 2. $5x + -4x + 7x$ $8x$

3. $6a + -7b + -3 + -2a$ $4a - 7b - 3$ 4. $0 + -5a$ $-5a$

5. $-(-5) + y$ $5 + y$ 6. $7a + 6x + -7a$ $6x$

7. $-12t^2 + 8t + -3t^2$ $-15t^2 + 8t$ 8. $2.3x + 5.1 + -4.6x$ $5.1 - 2.3x$

■PROPERTIES *Objective E*
In 9–14, an instance of what property is given?

9. If $x = -3$, then $-x = 3$.   **Op-op Property**

10. $-ab + 0 = -ab$ **Additive Identity Property**

11. $7y + -10y = -3y$ **Adding Like Terms Property**

12. If $s = -6$, then $-(s) = 6$.   **Op-op Property**

13. $xy + -xy = 0$ **Property of Opposites**

14. Jog 20 meters east, then 20 meters west, and you are back where you started.   **Property of Opposites**

■USES *Objective H*

15. A girl lost 10 lb, then gained 3 lb, then lost 4 lb. What is the total change in her weight?

-11 lb

16. A boy received gifts of g dollars and h dollars and spent x dollars, winding up with $3.50. Write an equation representing this situation.

$g + h - x = 3.50$

LESSON MASTER 2–3
QUESTIONS ON **SPUR** OBJECTIVES

■SKILLS *Objective A* (See pages 102–105 for objectives.)
In 1–8, write as a single fraction.

1. $\frac{2}{3} + \frac{3}{4}$ $\frac{17}{12}$ 2. $\frac{1}{3} + \frac{-1}{6} + \frac{3}{8}$ $\frac{13}{24}$

3. $-2\frac{3}{5} + -3\frac{8}{15}$ $\frac{-92}{15}$ 4. $\frac{x}{5} + \frac{4}{5}$ $\frac{x+4}{5}$

5. $\frac{p}{18} + \frac{5}{6}$ $\frac{p+15}{18}$ 6. $\frac{12}{c} + \frac{7}{c}$ $\frac{19}{c}$

7. $\frac{a}{m} + \frac{1}{n}$ $\frac{an+m}{mn}$ 8. $\frac{x}{r} + \frac{y}{s}$ $\frac{xs+ry}{rs}$

9. Juan owned a stock whose value rose $\frac{5}{8}$ point on Monday, rose $\frac{1}{4}$ point on Tuesday, and fell $1\frac{1}{2}$ points on Wednesday. What was the overall change in his stock's value for these three days?

$-\frac{5}{8}$

10. What is the perimeter of a rectangle with length $2\frac{1}{10}$ and width $1\frac{3}{5}$?

$7\frac{2}{5}$

11. Represent the perimeter of a triangle with sides $1\frac{1}{8}$, $2\frac{4}{5}$, and x as a simplified algebraic expression.

$\frac{157}{40} + x$

■PROPERTIES *Objective E*
In 12–15, identify what property of addition is given.

12. $\frac{5}{12} + 0 = \frac{5}{12}$ **Add. Identity Prop.**

13. $3x + 5 + 2x = 5x + 5$ **Adding Like Terms Prop.**

14. $-(-x) = x$ **Op-op Prop.**

15. $\frac{x}{13} + \frac{-x}{13} = 0$ **Prop. of Opposites**

LESSON MASTER 2–4
QUESTIONS ON **SPUR** OBJECTIVES

■REPRESENTATIONS *Objective K (See pages 102–105 for objectives.)*

1. Plot three vertices of a square (1, 3), (1, 6), and (4, 6). Find and plot the fourth vertex. Connect the vertices in order.

2. a. Toss four coins ten times. Plot the data as ordered pairs which show: (number of the toss, number of heads on the toss).

b. Which number of heads occurred most often?

sample: 2

Least often?

sample: 0 and 4

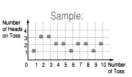
Sample:

3. a. The following ordered pairs show (year, net cash flow from U.S. Savings Bonds, in billions): (1975, 4), (1977, 4.7), 1979, -0.8), (1981, -4.3). Draw a graph for this data. Label the axes.

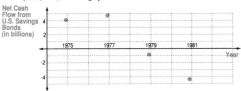

b. During which two-year period was the decrease greatest?

from 1977 to 1979

c. What do the negative numbers mean in 1979 and 1981?

The net cash flow is to (not from) U.S. Savings Bonds.

Algebra © Scott, Foresman and Company   *Continued* **13**

LESSON MASTER 2–4
(page 2)

4. a. A football team made the following gains and losses on their first four successive plays: 3, 4, -5, and 9. Plot the data (play number, yards made on that play).

b. Did the team make a first down? That is, did they gain more than 10 yards?

yes

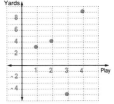

5. This graph shows the number of kilowatts of electricity being used by a family during a day.

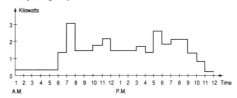

a. What do you think happened at 6 A.M.?

sample: Someone turned the lights on in the morning.

b. How many kilowatts were being used between 7 and 8 A.M.?

3 kilowatts

c. Why do you think it was so high?

sample: Someone used electrical appliances to cook.

d. At what time do you think the last person went to bed for the night?

11 P.M.

14   *Algebra © Scott, Foresman and Company*

LESSON MASTER 2–5
QUESTIONS ON **SPUR** OBJECTIVES

■REPRESENTATIONS *Objective L (See pages 102–105 for objectives.)*
In 1–4, find the image of the point after the given slide.

1. (-3, -1); 15 units left and 20 units up.   **(-18, 19)**

2. (-6, 14); 4 units left and 9 units down.   **(-10, 5)**

3. (7.3, -4.9); 3.5 units right and 4.6 units up.   **(10.8, -0.3)**

4. (x, y); 63 units right and 26 units down.   **(x + 63, y − 26)**

In 5–7, the image of a point after the indicated slide is given. Find the preimage. (**Hint: Work backwards.**)

5. (4, -2); 6 units left and 4 units up.   **(10, -6)**

6. (-5, -8); 4 units right and 3 units down.   **(-9, -5)**

7. (x + 6, y + 9); 3 units right and 6 units up.   **(x + 3, y + 3)**

In 8 and 9, find *a* and *b*.

8. (3 + a, 2 + b) = (-7, 10)   a = **-10**   b = **8**

9. (a + -4, b + -6) = (1, 0)   a = **5**   b = **6**

10. Graph the image of the triangle after a slide of 3 units right and 4 units down.

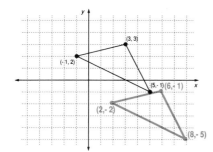

Algebra © Scott, Foresman and Company   **15**

LESSON MASTER 2–6
QUESTIONS ON **SPUR** OBJECTIVES

■SKILLS *Objective C (See pages 102–105 for objectives.)*
In 1–4, solve the equations in your head.

1. x + 5 = 11   **x = 6**   **2.** 2 + h + 3 = 60   **h = 55**

3. 15 = p + 6   **p = 9**   **4.** 20 = 5 + x + -4   **x = 19**

In 5–9, solve and check the equations.

5. x + -9 = 11   **x = 20**   **6.** -8 + c + 7 = -12   **c = -11**
     20 + -9 = 11   -8 + -11 + 7 = -12

7. -12.4 + s = -14   **s = -1.6**   **8.** p + -5.7 = -2.3   **p = 3.4**
     -12.4 + -1.6 = -14   3.4 + -5.7 = -2.3

9. $2 = \frac{1}{3} + \frac{t}{6} + \frac{1}{3}$ **t = 8**
     $2 = \frac{1}{3} + \frac{8}{6} + \frac{1}{3}$

In 10–13, solve for x.

10. x + a = c   **x = c + -a**   **11.** x + -p = r   **x = r + p**

12. k + x = m   **x = m + -k**   **13.** w = x + -v   **x = w + v**

■PROPERTIES *Objective F*
Multiple choice In 14 and 15, circle the equation that does not have the same solution as the others.

14. (a) 4 + x = -8   (b) x + 4 = -8   (c) -8 + x = 4   (d) -8 = 4 + x

15. (a) y + 6 = -3   (b) 6 + y = -3   (c) -3 = 6 + y   (d) 6 = y + -3

■USES *Objective H*
16. The temperature is -10°C. By how much must it increase to become 4°C?   **14°C**

In 17 and 18, a. write an equation to describe the situation. b. Solve.

17. Peggy opened a savings account with $40. She made a deposit of x dollars, and withdrew $20. Her balance now is $90.
a. **90 = 40 + x − 20**   b. **x = 70**

18. A triangle has sides of 13, 8, and y. The perimeter is 28.
a. **13 + 8 + y = 28**   b. **y = 7**

16   *Algebra © Scott, Foresman and Company*

LESSON MASTER 2-7
QUESTIONS ON **SPUR** OBJECTIVES

■SKILLS *Objective D* (See pages 102–105 for objectives.)
In 1–4, solve.

1. $-13 < d + 5$ $\underline{d > \text{-}18}$

2. $11 + w \le 20$ $\underline{w \le 9}$

3. $d + \text{-}9.3 \le \text{-}13.7$ $\underline{d \le \text{-}4.4}$

4. $\frac{2}{5} + a > \frac{3}{4}$ $\underline{a > \frac{7}{20}}$

5. Solve for x: $3a + x < \text{-}5a$ $\underline{x < \text{-}8a}$

6. Solve for y: $y + \text{-}8b \ge \text{-}12b$ $\underline{y \ge \text{-}4b}$

In 7–10, solve in your head.

7. $x + 4 \le 7$ $\underline{x \le 3}$

8. $\text{-}3 + y < 6$ $\underline{y < 9}$

9. $2.5 + p > 5.5$ $\underline{p > 3}$

10. $r + \frac{1}{2} \ge \frac{3}{4}$ $\underline{r \ge \frac{1}{4}}$

■PROPERTIES *Objective F*

11. If $s + 13 < \text{-}5$, then $s + 13 + \text{-}13 < \text{-}5 + \text{-}13$. This is an instance of what property?
$\underline{\text{The Addition Property of Inequality}}$

12. Mike adds -8 to both sides of $x + 8 \ge 11$. What sentence results? $\underline{x \ge 3}$

13. *Multiple choice* Circle the inequality that has the same solutions as $\text{-}4 < x < 10$.
(a) $10 < x < \text{-}4$ (b) $10 \ge x > \text{-}4$ (c) $10 > x > \text{-}4$ (d) $\text{-}4 \le x \le 10$

■USES *Objective H*

14. Edna saved $11 and received $5 as a gift. If jeans cost at least $25, how much more does she need? $\underline{\text{at least } \$9}$

15. The temperature was 10°C. It increased by $n°$. Now it is more than T°C.
a. Give a sentence relating 10, T, and n. $\underline{10 + n > T}$
b. Solve for n. $\underline{n > T - 10}$

■REPRESENTATIONS *Objective J*
In 16 and 17, solve and graph the solution set.

16. $y + \text{-}1.2 < 5.6$ $\underline{y < 6.8}$

17. $\frac{1}{2} + a \le \frac{\text{-}3}{2}$ $\underline{a \le \text{-}2}$

LESSON MASTER 2-8
QUESTIONS ON **SPUR** OBJECTIVES

■PROPERTIES *Objective G* (See pages 102–105 for objectives.)
In 1–3, find the possible values for n.

1.   2.   3.

$1 < n < 15$ $2.7 < n < 13.9$ $\frac{3}{4} < n < 5\frac{3}{4}$

■USES *Objective I*
In 4–8, solve using the triangle inequality.

4. It is 160 miles from St. Louis, Missouri, to Bloomington, Illinois. It is 140 miles from Bloomington to Chicago, Illinois. From only this information, what can you say about the distance from St. Louis to Chicago?
$\underline{\text{It is from 20 to 300 miles.}}$

5. Richard lives 3.5 km from the library and 1.4 km from school. The distance of the library from school must be greater than or equal to $\underline{2.1 \text{ km}}$ but less than or equal to $\underline{4.9 \text{ km}}$.

6. Why is there no triangle with sides of lengths 23 in., 34 in., and 10 in.?
$\underline{23 + 10 \not> 34}$

7. Two folding display racks are joined by a hinge as shown.

a. Name three inequalities AB must satisfy.
$\underline{AB < 20 + 24;\ 20 < AB + 24;\ 24 < AB + 20}$
b. AB can be no shorter than $\underline{4}$ in.
c. AB can be no longer than $\underline{44}$ in.

8. A television transmitter is 16 miles from one relay station and 12 miles from another. Describe the possible distances separating the two relay stations.
$\underline{\text{any distance from 4 to 28 miles}}$

LESSON MASTER 3-1
QUESTIONS ON **SPUR** OBJECTIVES

■SKILLS *Objective D* (See pages 150–152 for objectives.)
In 1–7, simplify.

1. $11x - 3x + 7x$ $\underline{15x}$

2. $\text{-}1.8r - .4r + 2.3r$ $\underline{0.1r}$

3. $3d - \frac{d}{4} - \frac{\text{-}5d}{2}$ $\underline{\frac{21d}{4}}$

4. $x^2 - \text{-}2x - 3x^2$ $\underline{\text{-}2x^2 + 2x}$

5. $4t - (\text{-}6t + 4)$ $\underline{10t - 4}$

6. $\text{-}63 - 44 + 17 - 40 - 6$ $\underline{\text{-}56}$

7. $\text{-}6z^2 - 4z^3 + 8z^3 - 9z^2$ $\underline{\text{-}15z^2 + 12z^3}$

■PROPERTIES *Objective E*
In 8–10, rewrite each subtraction as addition.

8. $4 - 6 - \text{-}10$ $\underline{4 + \text{-}6 + 10}$

9. $2a - 3b + c$ $\underline{2a + \text{-}3b + c}$

10. $\text{-}3 - h + 4h - \text{-}6$ $\underline{\text{-}3 + \text{-}h + 4h + 6}$

11. Write a key sequence to compute $\text{-}47 - \text{-}86$ using the $\boxed{+}$ and $\boxed{+/-}$ keys on your calculator.
$\underline{47\ \boxed{+/-}\ \boxed{+}\ 86\ \boxed{=}}$

12. Evaluate $\text{-}f - g$ when $f = \text{-}10$ and $g = 12$. $\underline{\text{-}2}$

13. Evaluate $\text{-}(2u - 3v)$ when $u = 4$ and $v = 7$. $\underline{13}$

14. Evaluate $6 - (\text{-}x - y)$ when $x = 2$ and $y = \text{-}5$. $\underline{3}$

LESSON MASTER 3-2
QUESTIONS ON **SPUR** OBJECTIVES

■USES *Objective F* (See pages 150–152 for objectives.)

1. The label on a can of paint says it will cover 550 square feet. Tim has used part of the can to paint a wall of W square feet. How much more area can be covered by what is left in the can?
$\underline{(550 - W) \text{ square feet}}$

2. A dealer sells a TV set for S dollars. This price includes overhead expenses E and a profit P. How much did the TV cost the dealer?
$\underline{(S - (E + P)) \text{ dollars or } (S - E - P) \text{ dollars}}$

3. After cutting 115 square meters of a lawn, Carlos has less than 28 square meters to cut. If the lawn area is M square meters, write an inequality to describe the possible values of M.
$\underline{M - 115 < 28}$

4. Last year Mrs. Chen's arithmetic class mean was 7 points below passing on a basic skills test. This year it was 8 points above passing. By how much did it improve this year?
$\underline{15 \text{ points}}$

5. In the first football game, the fullback's average gain per carry was -2.3 yards. In the second game it was 3.2 yards. By how much did it increase?
$\underline{5.5 \text{ yards}}$

6. The highest temperature ever recorded in Fairbanks, Alaska, is 84°F. The lowest temperature is -40°F. What is the difference between these two temperatures?
$\underline{124°F}$

7. The closing price for ABC stock was d dollars. If the change for the day was $\text{-}3\frac{1}{8}$, what was the opening price?
$\underline{\left(d + 3\frac{1}{8}\right) \text{ dollars}}$

8. In a presidential poll, $n\%$ favored candidate A, $m\%$ favored candidate B, and the rest had no opinion. What percent had no opinion?
$\underline{(100 - (n + m))\% \text{ or } (100 - n - m)\%}$

LESSON MASTER 3-3
QUESTIONS ON **SPUR** OBJECTIVES

■SKILLS   *Objective B*   *(See pages 150–152 for objectives.)*
In 1–4, solve and check.

1. $p - 34 = -8$ $p = 26$
$26 - 34 = -8$

2. $4.5 = r - 3.8$ $r = 8.3$
$4.5 = 8.3 - 3.8$

3. $x - 11 > -5$ $x > 6$
$6 - 11 = -5$, and
$7 - 11 > -5$

4. $\frac{5}{8} \ge y - \frac{3}{4}$ $y \le \frac{11}{8}$
$\frac{5}{8} = \frac{11}{8} - \frac{3}{4}$, and $\frac{5}{8} > \frac{5}{4} - \frac{3}{4}$

In 5–10, solve for x.

5. $x - a = 19$ $x = 19 + a$

6. $k = x - 12$ $x = k + 12$

7. $x - p = 3p$ $x = 4p$

8. $-\frac{3}{4}d = x - \frac{d}{2}$ $x = -\frac{d}{4}$

9. $g < x - 32$ $x > g + 32$

10. $x - c > b$ $x > b + c$

■SKILLS   *Objective D*
In 11–14, simplify.

11. $6h + h - 4h$ $3h$

12. $4 + (x - 8)$ $x - 4$

13. $3x + 5 - 2x$ $x + 5$

14. $-9x - x + 10x$ 0

■USES   *Objective F*

15. The range of scores on an algebra test was R. The minimum score was 60.
Write and solve an equation to find the maximum score h.
$h = R + 60$

16. To lose weight, Sonya had to reduce her daily caloric intake to less than 1800 calories. By eliminating desserts she removed 600 calories and is now losing weight. If her previous intake was c calories, write an inequality describing the situation.
$c - 600 < 1800; c < 2400$

17. Mr. Swenson has saved \$1500 for a down payment on an automobile. If the automobile costs T dollars, how much will he have to borrow?
$(T - 1500)$ dollars

Algebra © Scott, Foresman and Company   **21**

LESSON MASTER 3-4
QUESTIONS ON **SPUR** OBJECTIVES

■SKILLS   *Objective A*   *(See pages 150–152 for objectives.)*
In 1–6, find the intersection of the sets.

1. $A = \{4, 9, 13, 17\}$, $B = \{1, 9, 15, 17\}$ $\{9, 17\}$

2. $C = \{1, 3, 5\}$, $D = \{3, 5, 7, 9, 11\}$ $\{3, 5\}$

3. $F = \{12, 14\}$, $G = \{14, 16\}$, $H = \{14, 15\}$ $\{14\}$

4. $J = \{20, 30, 40\}$, $K = \{10, 20, 30, 40\}$ $\{20, 30, 40\}$

5. $L = \{101, 102, 103\}$, $M = \{104, 105, 106\}$ $\emptyset$

6. $P = \emptyset$, $Q = \{2, 4, 6\}$ $\emptyset$

■REPRESENTATIONS   *Objective H*
In 7–11, graph the solutions. The domain is the real numbers.

7. $x < 12$ and $x < 7$
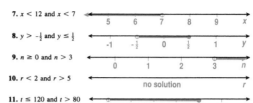

8. $y > -\frac{1}{2}$ and $y \le \frac{1}{2}$

9. $n \ge 0$ and $n > 3$

10. $r < 2$ and $r > 5$
no solution

11. $t \le 120$ and $t > 80$

■REPRESENTATIONS   *Objective I*
In 12 and 13, draw a Venn diagram showing the two sets.

12. $A = \{-3, -1, 0, 5\}$
$B = \{-8, -1, 0, 7\}$

13. $C = \{1, 2, 3, 4\}$
$D = \{0, 1, 2, 3, 4, 5\}$

14. Refer to the Venn diagram.
What can you say about $X \cap Y$?
$X \cap Y = \emptyset$

15. Shade in $Z \cap W$.

22   *Algebra © Scott, Foresman and Company*

LESSON MASTER 3-5
QUESTIONS ON **SPUR** OBJECTIVES

■SKILLS   *Objective A*   *(See pages 150–152 for objectives.)*
In 1–6, $A = \{-1, 1, 7, 12\}$, $B = \{-5, 1, 7, 10, 20\}$, and $C = \{-3, 1, 7, 10, 30\}$. Describe:

1. $A \cup B$.
$\{-5, -1, 1, 7, 10, 12, 20\}$

2. $B \cup C$.
$\{-5, -3, 1, 7, 10, 20, 30\}$

3. $A \cup (B \cap C)$.
$\{-1, 1, 7, 10, 12\}$

4. $(A \cup B) \cap C$.
$\{1, 7, 10\}$

5. $(C \cup A) \cap B$.
$\{1, 7, 10\}$

6. $(C \cap B) \cup (A \cap B)$.
$\{1, 7, 10\}$

■REPRESENTATIONS   *Objective H*
In 7–11, graph all solutions on a number line. The domain is the set of real numbers.

7. $x > 2$ or $x \ge 5$

8. $y \le 3$ or $y > 6$

9. $h > -1$ or $h < 1$

10. $0 \le t < 3$ or $t > 7$

11. $-2 < z \le 2$ or $4 \le z < 6$

■REPRESENTATIONS   *Objective I*
In 12 and 13, $A = \{-2, 0, 2, 4\}$, $B = \{-1, 0, 1, 2\}$, and $C = \{0, 1, 2, 3, 4\}$.
Draw and shade a Venn diagram to illustrate each expression.

12. $(A \cup B) \cap C$.

13. $A \cup (B \cap C)$.
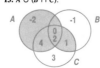

Algebra © Scott, Foresman and Company   **23**

LESSON MASTER 3-6
QUESTIONS ON **SPUR** OBJECTIVES

■USES   *Objective G*   *(See pages 150–152 for objectives.)*
In 1 and 2, find $N(A \cup B)$ if A and B are mutually exclusive.

1. $N(A) = 4$, $N(B) = 9$ 13

2. $N(A) = 72$, $N(B) = 36$ 108

In 3 and 4, find $N(A \cup B)$.

3. $N(A) = 32$, $N(B) = 24$, $N(A \cap B) = 8$ 48

4. $N(A) = 153$, $N(B) = 147$, $N(A \cap B) = 94$ 206

5. On the Sluggers baseball squad, a total of 8 players can play infield (includes pitchers and catchers), 7 can play outfield and 3 can play either infield or outfield. How many players are on the squad?
12 players

6. There are 28 students in the Drama Club and 32 students in the Chorus. If there are 50 students altogether, how many are in both?
10 students

7. In a poll of fast food preferences, 100 liked hamburgers, 75 liked pizza, 50 like chicken, 10 liked hamburgers and pizza only, 10 liked hamburgers and chicken only, 5 liked pizza and chicken only, and 10 liked all three. How many people were polled? Draw a Venn diagram to illustrate the situation.

180 people

In 8 and 9, find $P(A \cup B)$.

8. $P(A) = \frac{1}{2}$, $P(B) = \frac{1}{3}$, $P(A \cap B) = 0$ $\frac{5}{6}$

9. $P(A) = \frac{1}{4}$, $P(B) = \frac{4}{9}$, $P(A \cap B) = \frac{5}{36}$ $\frac{5}{9}$

10. What is the probability of rolling either an even number or a prime number with a single die? $\frac{5}{6}$

11. In a group of 100 car owners, 47 change their own oil, 61 wash their own car, and 38 do both. If someone were chosen at random from this group, what is the probability they either change their oil or wash their own car? $\frac{7}{10}$

24   *Algebra © Scott, Foresman and Company*

LESSON MASTER 3-7
QUESTIONS ON **SPUR** OBJECTIVES

■REPRESENTATIONS *Objective J (See pages 150–152 for objectives.)*
In 1–4, graph each equation on the same set of axes. The domain is the set of real numbers.

1. $x + y = -2$ 2. $x + y = 0$

3. $y = 3 - x$ 4. $y = 4 - x$

$y = 4 - x$
$y = 3 - x$
$x + y = 0$
$x + y = -2$

5. Lisa and Terry have a total of 8 albums in their combined collections. Graph all the pairs that show the possible ways the albums may be divided between them.

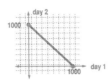

6. A cross-country trucker covered 1000 miles in two days. Graph all possible pairs that show the miles the trucker could have driven on each day.

7. Write an equation that describes the points graphed at the right.

$\underline{x - y = -2}$

LESSON MASTER 3-8
QUESTIONS ON **SPUR** OBJECTIVES

■SKILLS *Objective C (See pages 150–152 for objectives.)*
In 1–4, find the measure of a supplement of the given angle.

1. $m\angle A = 43°$ __137°__   2. $m\angle B = 135°$ __45°__

3. $m\angle P = c°$ __$(180 - c)°$__   4. $m\angle R = 3x°$ __$(180 - 3x)°$__

In 5–8, find the measure of a complement of the given angle.

5. $m\angle C = 33°$ __57°__   6. $m\angle D = 88°$ __2°__

7. $m\angle S = n°$ __$(90 - n)°$__   8. $m\angle T = 4y°$ __$(90 - 4y)°$__

9. In the figure find the measures of x, y, and z.

$x = $ __105°__

$y = $ __75°__

$z = $ __105°__

In 10–12, find the unknown measure of the angle of the triangle.

10. __70°__   11. __58°__   12. __52°__

13. In the figure, find a, x, and y.

$a = $ __44°__

$x = $ __108°__

$y = $ __116°__

In 14 and 15, find a in each figure.

14. __65°__   15. __45°__

LESSON MASTER 4-1
QUESTIONS ON **SPUR** OBJECTIVES

■PROPERTIES *Objective F (See pages 204–207 for objectives.)*
In 1–4, identify what property of multiplication is given.

1. $a(bc) = (bc)a$ __Commutative__   2. $2 \cdot 3h = 6h$ __Associative__

3. $k(x + y) = (x + y)k$ __Commutative__   4. $4(25 \cdot 3) = (4 \cdot 25)3$ __Associative__

In 5–8, simplify.

5. $3x \cdot 4y$ __12xy__   6. $am \cdot an$ __a^2mn__

7. $2ab \cdot 3bc \cdot 4ac$ __$24a^2b^2c^2$__   8. $\frac{1}{2}a \cdot \frac{2}{3}b$ __$\frac{1}{3}ab$__

■USES *Objective G*
9. Find the area of a walk 3 ft wide around a rectangular pool 27 ft by 32 ft. __390 square feet__

10. Find the area of the shaded part.   11. How many trees are in the orchard around the barn?

__78 square units__   __31 trees__

■USES *Objective K*
12. A calculator comes in a box 2 cm × 8 cm × 10 cm. How many calculators can be shipped in a box 30 cm × 48 cm × 60 cm? __540 calculators__

13. A standard room is 10 ft high. What does the area of the floor have to be for the volume to be 7200 cubic feet? __720 square feet__

■REPRESENTATIONS *Objective L*
In 14 and 15, the squares have length 1. What multiplication of fractions does each drawing represent, and what is the area of the shaded part?

14. $\frac{2}{3} \cdot \frac{3}{4}$ 15. $\frac{5}{5} \cdot \frac{5}{6}$

$\frac{1}{2}$ $\frac{1}{3}$

LESSON MASTER 4-2
QUESTIONS ON **SPUR** OBJECTIVES

■SKILLS *Objective A (See pages 204–207 for objectives.)*
In 1–8, multiply.

1. $\frac{5}{8x} \cdot \frac{2x}{3}$ __$\frac{5}{12}$__   2. $\frac{4ab}{9} \cdot \frac{3}{5a}$ __$\frac{4b}{15}$__

3. $\frac{ax}{3} \cdot \frac{2}{ay}$ __$\frac{2x}{3y}$__   4. $3\frac{1}{3} \cdot 1\frac{1}{5}$ __4__

5. $\frac{7m}{12} \cdot \frac{3n}{4m} \cdot \frac{1}{7n}$ __$\frac{1}{16}$__   6. $42g \cdot \frac{3}{7}$ __18g__

7. $\frac{24}{11k} \cdot \frac{22r}{9} \cdot \frac{3k}{8}$ __2r__   8. $\frac{8p}{15} \cdot 45$ __24p__

■USES *Objective G*
9. In 1984 in the U.S., there were 22.8 motor vehicle deaths per 100,000 population. How many motor vehicle deaths would you then expect in a U.S. city of 3.5 million people? __798 deaths__

10. A baseball player's batting average (hits/times at bat) is .300. At that rate, how many times at bat would the player need to get 120 hits? __400 hits__

11. There are 85 calories in one cooked egg, and 3 eggs in an omelet. How many calories are in 2 omelettes? __510 calories__

12. In 1982, there were 77.2 lb of beef per person consumed in the United States. The average family consisted of 3.1 people. Farmers received 57 cents per lb for beef. On the average, how many cents did the farmers receive from each family's purchase of beef? __13,641.24¢__

■USES *Objective K*
13. Susan has 75 stamps in her collection and adds 7 stamps to her collection every month. In how many months will she have 110 stamps? Write an equation to represent this problem and solve the problem.

__$75 + 7m = 110$__

__5 months__

LESSON MASTER 4–3
QUESTIONS ON **SPUR** OBJECTIVES

■**PROPERTIES** *Objective F (See pages 204–207 for objectives.)*
In 1–8, simplify and name the multiplication property used.

1. $4 \cdot \frac{a}{a}$ ___4___ ; __Multiplicative Identity Prop.__

2. $6x \cdot \frac{1}{6x}$ ___1___ ; __Property of Reciprocals__

3. $-1 \cdot -2y$ ___2y___ ; __Multiplication Property of -1__

4. $8(2n - 2n)$ ___0___ ; __Multiplication Property of 0__

5. $(-6)(ab)$ ___-6ab___ ; __Associative Property of Mult.__

6. $\frac{4k}{4k}(2c - 1)$ ___2c − 1___ ; __Multiplicative Identity Prop.__

7. $(x + y) \cdot \frac{1}{(x + y)}$ ___1___ ; __Property of Reciprocals__

8. $(2t + 1)(3t - 1)(0)$ ___0___ ; __Multiplication Property of 0__

In 9–12, write the reciprocal.

9. -1.5 ___$-\frac{2}{3}$___   10. $\frac{8}{3}$ ___$\frac{3}{8}$___

11. $\frac{5}{2x}$ ___$\frac{2x}{5}$___   12. $\frac{6}{y-1}$ ___$\frac{y-1}{6}$___

In 13–18, for what value of the variable is the reciprocal undefined?

13. $\frac{2x}{15}$ ___$x = 0$___   14. $\frac{n}{-5}$ ___$n = 0$___

15. $\frac{a-5}{7}$ ___$a = 5$___   16. $\frac{c+4}{9b}$ ___$c = -4$___

17. y ___$y = 0$___   18. $\frac{0}{x}$ ___all of them___

LESSON MASTER 4–4
QUESTIONS ON **SPUR** OBJECTIVES

■**SKILLS** *Objective B (See pages 204–207 for objectives.)*
In 1–8, solve and check.

1. $17n = 51$ ___$n = 3; 17 \cdot 3 = 51$___

2. $-13k = 65$ ___$k = -5; (-13)(-5) = 65$___

3. $-5s = -1.25$ ___$s = .25; (-5)(.25) = -1.25$___

4. $-8.978 = 1.34t$ ___$t = -6.7; -8.978 = 1.34(-6.7)$___

5. $\frac{3}{4}x = 27$ ___$x = 36; \frac{3}{4}(36) = 27$___

6. $-7c = 4\frac{1}{5}$ ___$c = -\frac{3}{5}; -7\left(-\frac{3}{5}\right) = 4\frac{1}{5}$___

7. $-\frac{6}{25} = -\frac{4}{5}p$ ___$p = \frac{3}{10}; -\frac{6}{25} = -\frac{4}{5}\left(\frac{3}{10}\right)$___

8. $6y - 8y = 2$ ___$y = -1; 6(-1) - 8(-1) = 2$___

In 9–12, solve for x.

9. $3x = a$ ___$x = \frac{a}{3}$___   10. $-bx = h$ ___$x = -\frac{h}{b}$___

11. $\frac{x}{n} = 12$ ___$x = 12n$___   12. $\frac{a}{b}x = c$ ___$x = \frac{bc}{a}$___

■**PROPERTIES** *Objective F*
13. What property tells you that $6x = 18.6$ is equivalent to $x = 3.1$?

___Multiplication Property of Equality___

14. To solve $\frac{a}{b}x = \frac{c}{d}$ for x, multiply both sides by ___$\frac{b}{a}$___ .

■**USES** *Objective K*
15. A plane flies from St. Louis to Chicago, a distance of 297 miles, in 45 minutes. Use the formula $d = rt$ to find its average speed. ___396 mph___

16. Use the formula $I = prt$ to determine the annual rate of interest r a bank pays if $120 earns $6 in one year. ___5%___

LESSON MASTER 4–5
QUESTIONS ON **SPUR** OBJECTIVES

■**SKILLS** *Objective B (See pages 204–207 for objectives.)*
In 1–4, solve and check.

1. $2x + 3x - 5x = 7.2$ ___$\emptyset; 0 \cdot x = 7.2$ has no solution___

2. $0 = 9y - 6y - 3y$ ___all reals; $0 = 0 \cdot y$ is always true___

3. $3n = 8 - 5 - 3$ ___$n = 0; 3 \cdot 0 = 8 - 5 - 3$___

4. $(3 - 4)x = 5$ ___$x = -5; (3 - 4) \cdot -5 = -1 \cdot -5 = 5$___

■**SKILLS** *Objective C*
In 5–10, solve and check.

5. $6 - x = 32$ ___$x = -26; 6 - (-26) = 32$___

6. $9.3 = 11.5 - y$ ___$y = 2.2; 9.3 = 11.5 - 2.2$___

7. $330 - s = 0$ ___$s = 330; 330 - 330 = 0$___

8. $-\frac{2}{7} - a = -\frac{3}{7}$ ___$a = \frac{1}{7}; -\frac{2}{7} - \left(\frac{1}{7}\right) = -\frac{3}{7}$___

9. $-18.7 - t = -4.9$ ___$t = -13.8; -18.7 - (-13.8) = -4.9$___

10. $\frac{5}{12} = \frac{3}{4} - k$ ___$k = \frac{1}{3}; \frac{5}{12} = \frac{3}{4} - \frac{1}{3}$___

In 11–16, solve for x.

11. $a - x = b$ ___$x = a - b$___   12. $-c = -d - x$ ___$x = c - d$___

13. $\frac{2}{5} - x = \frac{3}{7}$ ___$x = -\frac{1}{35}$___   14. $\frac{12}{25} = -\frac{24}{25} - x$ ___$x = -\frac{36}{25}$___

15. $1.1a - x = 3.7a$ ___$x = -2.6a$___   16. $0 = -t - x$ ___$x = -t$___

17. Solve for z: $\frac{1}{2} - z = -\frac{4}{7}$ ___$z = \frac{15}{14}$___

18. If $50 - t = \frac{17}{3}$, what does t equal? ___$t = \frac{133}{3}$___

LESSON MASTER 4–6
QUESTIONS ON **SPUR** OBJECTIVES

■**SKILLS** *Objective D (See pages 204–207 for objectives.)*
In 1–8, solve and check.

1. $6c \le 42$ ___$c \le 7; 6 \cdot 7 = 42, 6 \cdot 6 \le 42$___

2. $-68 > 17d$ ___$d < -4; -68 = 17(-4), -68 > 17(-5)$___

3. $-9k > 108$ ___$k < -12; -9(-12) = 108, -9(-13) > 108$___

4. $5.5x \le 45.1$ ___$x \le 8.2; 5.5(8.2) = 45.1, 5.5(8.1) \le 45.1$___

5. $-.36 < .144n$ ___$n > -2.5; -.36 = .114(-2.5), -.36 < .114(-2.4)$___

6. $-.7y \ge -6.3$ ___$y \le 9; -.7(9) = -6.3, -.7(8) \ge -6.3$___

7. $\frac{2}{5}a \ge 8$ ___$a \ge 20; \frac{2}{5}(20) = 8, \frac{2}{5}(21) \ge 8$___

8. $-\frac{5}{12} < -\frac{3}{8}b$ ___$b < \frac{10}{9}; -\frac{5}{12} = \left(-\frac{3}{8}\right)\left(\frac{10}{9}\right), -\frac{5}{12} < -\frac{3}{8}(1)$___

■**PROPERTIES** *Objective F*
9. If $-x < a$, then x ___>___ $-a$.

10. What inequality results if both sides of $-3z \ge -2$ are multiplied by $-\frac{1}{3}$? ___$z \le \frac{2}{3}$___

■**USES** *Objective K*
11. At least how much must the radius of a circle be in order for the circumference to be at least 88? ___$\frac{44}{\pi}$ or ≈ 14___

12. The class has collected $75.50 for a pizza party. A large pizza costs $9.95.

a. Write an inequality to find how many pizzas the class can buy. ___$9.95x \le 75.50$___

b. Solve the inequality. ___$x \approx 7.6; 7$ pizzas___

13. In 4 minutes, a drain can empty at most 40 gallons from a tank.

a. Write an inequality that tells the rate at which the drain empties water from the tank. ___$r \le \frac{40 \text{ gallons}}{4 \text{ minutes}}$___

b. Solve the inequality. ___$r \le 10$ gallons/minute___

LESSON MASTER 4-7
QUESTIONS ON SPUR OBJECTIVES

■USES *Objective H* (See pages 204–207 for objectives.)

1. Combination locks have 36 numbers used in three-number combinations. How many different combinations are there? (Assume that the same number cannot be used twice in a row.)

44,100 combinations

2. A car can be ordered in six different colors, with a choice of two engines and three transmissions. How many different cars can be ordered?

36 cars

3. On a special sale, pizza can be ordered with two toppings. Suppose there are eight different toppings available.
a. How many pizzas can be ordered with two different toppings?

28 pizzas

b. Suppose you can also order "doubles" (pizzas with a double order of the same topping). How many different pizzas can be ordered?

36 pizzas

4. A certain state uses three letters followed by three digits for its license plates. The letters I, O, and Q are not used, because they might be read as one or zero. How many license plates are possible?

12,167,000 license plates

5. How many different batting lineups can a 9-member baseball team have if the pitcher must bat last?

40,320 batting lineups

6. Suppose a flag is to be made with three stripes of equal areas. Each of the colors red, white, and blue must be used, but can be chosen in any order. If the stripes can be either all vertical or all horizontal, how many different flags can be made?

12 flags

7. The digits 0, 1, and 8 read the same right side up or upside down.
a. How many different two-digit numbers read the same either way? (A number may not begin with zero.)

6 numbers

b. How many different three-digit numbers can be read the same either way? (A number may not begin with zero.)

18 numbers

LESSON MASTER 4-8
QUESTIONS ON SPUR OBJECTIVES

■USES *Objective I* (See pages 204–207 for objectives.)
In 1–4, find P(A and B).

1. $P(A) = \frac{3}{5}$, $P(B$ given $A) = \frac{5}{8}$ $\frac{3}{8}$

2. $P(B) = .45$, $P(A$ given $B) = .30$ **.135**

3. $P(B) = .6n$, $P(A$ given $B) = .4n$ **.24n^2**

4. $P(A) = \frac{p}{3}$, $P(B$ given $A) = \frac{1}{p}$ $\frac{1}{3}$

In 5 and 6, find P(B given A).

5. $P(A$ and $B) = \frac{5}{8}$, $P(A) = \frac{3}{4}$ $\frac{5}{6}$

6. $P(A$ and $B) = \frac{p}{3}$, $P(A) = \frac{2p}{5}$ $\frac{5}{6}$

In 7 and 8, find P(A).

7. $P(A$ and $B) = \frac{1}{12}$, $P(B$ given $A) = \frac{2}{3}$ $\frac{1}{8}$

8. $P(A$ and $B) = .32r$, $P(B$ given $A) = .56r$ $\frac{4}{7}$; or about .57

9. If two light bulbs in a display are connected in series and one goes out, the other will also go out. The probability that a light bulb will last a month is .95. What is the probability that the display will last a month?

.9025

10. In basketball, a one-and-one free throw means that if you make the first one, you get to shoot again. Suppose a player usually makes 75% of his free throws. What is the probability that he will make both shots of a one-and-one free throw?

$\frac{9}{16}$, .5625 or 56.25%

11. At a carnival booth, you get a prize if you hit a target and knock it off the shelf. The probability that you will hit the target is $\frac{1}{4}$. The probability that it will fall off the shelf if you hit it is $\frac{1}{2}$. What is the probability that you will win a prize?

$\frac{1}{8}$

12. Two letters are picked at random from the letters in the word *mathematics*, without replacement. What is the probability that they are both vowels?

$\frac{6}{55}$

LESSON MASTER 4-9
QUESTIONS FOR SPUR OBJECTIVES

■SKILLS *Objective E* (See pages 204–207 for objectives.)
In 1–6, write as a decimal.

1. 6!   **720**   **2.** 3! · 2!   **12**

3. 2! + 5!   **122**   **4.** 7 · 6 · 5!   **5040**

5. $\frac{5!}{3!2!}$ **10**   **6.** $\frac{15!}{13!}$ **210**

In 7 and 8, simplify.

7. $\frac{(n+1)!}{n!}$ $n+1$ **8.** $n \cdot (n-1)!$ $n!$

In 9–12, use a calculator to estimate.

9. 16! $\approx 2.1 \times 10^{13}$ **10.** 8!7! $\approx 2.03 \times 10^8$

11. $\frac{10!}{6!4!}$ **210**   **12.** $\frac{9!+4!}{6!}$ ≈ 504

■USES *Objective J*

13. a. Eight gymnasts compete in an event. In how many ways can first and second place be awarded?   **56**

b. In how many different orders can all eight gymnasts finish?   **40,320**

14. a. Twelve members of a college basketball squad line up for the national anthem. How many different ways could this be done? 4.79×10^8

b. The members select a captain and co-captain from their 12. How many ways can this be done?   **132**

15. In how many ways can 6 different books be arranged on a shelf?   **720**

16. a. How many ways can the letters in the word CATS be arranged?   **24**

b. Write the arrangements that are English words.

CATS, ACTS, SCAT, CAST

17. Four boys and four girls are to be seated in a row on a stage, alternating boy, girl, boy, girl, etc. How many different seating arrangements are there?

576 seating arrangements

LESSON MASTER 5-1
QUESTIONS ON SPUR OBJECTIVES

■SKILLS *Objective A* (See pages 256–259 for objectives.)

1. If two numbers have the same sign, what is the sign of the quotient?   **positive**

2. If the result of dividing two numbers is negative, what can you say about the signs of the two numbers?   **they are opposite**

In 3 and 4, rewrite as a multiplication.

3. $\frac{x}{y} \div \frac{1}{z}$ $\frac{x}{y} \cdot z$ **4.** $\frac{\frac{\ell}{m}}{n}$ $\ell \cdot \frac{n}{m}$

In 5–18, simplify.

5. $\frac{3}{5} \div \frac{5}{9}$ $\frac{27}{25}$ **6.** $\frac{4a}{15b} \div \frac{6a}{25b}$ $\frac{10}{9}$

7. $\frac{-7}{12} \div \frac{14}{15}$ $-\frac{5}{8}$ **8.** $\frac{8}{11} \div \frac{-4}{5}$ $-\frac{10}{11}$

9. $\frac{\frac{3}{16}}{\frac{15}{4}}$ $\frac{1}{20}$ **10.** $\frac{\frac{-2\pi}{9}}{\frac{-4}{3}}$ $\frac{\pi}{6}$

11. $\frac{\frac{18}{1}}{\frac{1}{3}}$ **54**   **12.** $\frac{\frac{-28}{5}}{\frac{5}{4}}$ $-\frac{112}{5}$

13. $\frac{35x}{39} \div \frac{-42}{65y}$ $-\frac{25xy}{18}$ **14.** $\frac{\frac{-24n}{25p}}{\frac{-6}{5r}}$ $\frac{4nr}{5p}$

15. $\frac{\frac{3}{a}}{-20}$ $-\frac{3}{20a}$ **16.** $\frac{\frac{\ell}{5}}{6}$ $\frac{6t}{5}$

17. $\frac{\frac{-15w}{38x}}{\frac{45z}{57y}}$ $-\frac{wy}{2xz}$ **18.** $\frac{\frac{-9f}{56g}}{\frac{-15h}{49k}}$ $\frac{21fk}{40gh}$

LESSON MASTER 5-2
QUESTIONS ON **SPUR** OBJECTIVES

■**PROPERTIES**   *Objective D* (See pages 256–259 for objectives.)
In 1–6, what value(s) can the variable not have?

1. $\frac{2}{x}$ _____**x can't be 0**_____   2. $\frac{a}{a-4}$ _____**a can't be 4**_____

3. $\frac{b-3}{b+5}$ _____**b can't be -5**_____   4. $\frac{n+9}{n-11}$ _____**n can't be 11**_____

5. $\frac{1.5k}{k-1.5}$ _____**k can't be 1.5**_____   6. $\frac{c-6.1}{8.3+c}$ _____**c can't be -8.3**_____

■**USES**   *Objective F*

7. Andre Dawson of the Chicago Cubs earned $1,850,000 in 1988. If he played in all 162 games, how much was his salary per game?   **$11,419.75**

8. There are 30 slices in a certain loaf of bread and 2400 calories per loaf. How many calories are in each slice?   **80 calories/slice**

9. Bobby ran $\frac{3}{10}$ of a mile in $1\frac{1}{2}$ minutes. How many minutes per mile is this?   **5 minutes/mile**

10. In a recent year, there were 46,000 deaths from motor vehicle accidents in the U.S. If the population was approximately 226.5 million, what was the death rate per 100,000 population due to motor vehicle accidents?   **20.3 deaths / 100,000 people**

■**REPRESENTATIONS**   *Objective L*
11. For the program, what will be printed if the input is

a. 6? _____**IMPOSSIBLE**_____   b. -4? _____**.2**_____
```
10   PRINT "EVALUATE AN EXPRESSION."
20   PRINT "ENTER A VALUE OF A."
30   INPUT A
40   IF A = 6 THEN PRINT "IMPOSSIBLE"
50   IF A <> 6 THEN PRINT (A+2)/(A-6)
60   END
```

12. Write a program to evaluate $(n + 4)/(n + 9)$ for any value of n that is entered. If the input makes the expression meaningless, the computer should print "IMPOSSIBLE."
```
SAMPLE:  10   PRINT "ENTER A VALUE OF N."
         20   INPUT N
         30   IF N = -9 THEN PRINT "IMPOSSIBLE"
         40   IF N <> -9 THEN PRINT (N + 4)/(N + 9)
         50   END
```

Algebra © Scott, Foresman and Company   **37**

LESSON MASTER 5-3
QUESTIONS ON **SPUR** OBJECTIVES

■**USES**   *Objective G* (See pages 256–259 for objectives.)
1. In a recent year, there were 11,068 births and 9,928 deaths in Alaska. Write the ratio of births to deaths. $\frac{11068}{9928} \approx 1.115$

2. Jack gets an allowance of $7.50 a week and spends $3.50 a week for lunches. What percent of his allowance is spent for lunch? $\frac{3.50}{7.50} = 46.\overline{6}\%$

3. In the 1980 presidential election there were 35.5 million votes cast for the Democratic candidate and 43.9 million votes for the Republican. What was the ratio of Republican to Democratic votes? $\frac{43.9}{35.5} \approx 1.24$

4. *Multiple choice*   The rectangle that is considered to be most pleasing to the eye has a length to width ratio of about 1.618. Which rectangle has dimensions which are closest to this ratio?
   (a) 6 cm by 9 cm   (b) 8.5 in. by 11 in.
   (c) 3 in. by 5 in.   (d) 4 ft by 8 ft   _____**c**_____

5. A pair of jeans which usually sells for $24 is on sale for $6 less. What is the percent of discount?   **25%**

6. What is the percent of discount of a $119.95 suit which is selling for $99?   **≈17%**

7. What is the sales tax rate if you pay 60¢ on a $12.00 item?   **5%**

8. What is the sales tax rate for a tax of t dollars on an item costing c dollars? $\left(100\frac{t}{c}\right)\%$

9. A school swim team won 6 out of 8 swimming meets. What is the team's winning percentage?   **75%**

10. Mr. Gaston bought a stock for d dollars, and sold it for $d + p$ dollars. What was the ratio of his profit to his purchase price? $\frac{p}{d}$

38   *Algebra* © Scott, Foresman and Company

LESSON MASTER 5-4
QUESTIONS ON **SPUR** OBJECTIVES

■**SKILLS**   *Objective B* (See pages 256–259 for objectives.)
1. What is 60% of 25?   2. 16 is what percent of 40?
   _____**15**_____   _____**40%**_____

3. 38 is what percent of 20?   4. 65% of what number is 195?
   _____**190%**_____   _____**300**_____

5. What is 140% of 72?   6. 4.5% of what number is .09?
   _____**100.8**_____   _____**2**_____

7. 4.62 is what percent of 1.76?   8. What is 0.5% of 40?
   _____**262.5%**_____   _____**.2**_____

■**USES**   *Objective H*
9. A dealer wants to raise the price of a car by 6.5%. How much should the dealer add to the price of a $7800 car?

   _____**$507**_____

10. The population of Omaha, Nebraska went from 346,929 in 1970 to 313,939 in 1980. The 1980 population was what percent of the 1970 population?

   _____**90.5%**_____

11. The United States has about 134 million metric tons of copper deposits. This represents about 18.5% of the world deposits. How many million metric tons of copper deposits does the world have?

   _____**724.3 million metric tons**_____

12. Sara withdrew $50 from her savings account of $168. About what percent did she withdraw?

   _____**30%**_____

13. In the first 50 years of the all-star baseball games, 53 games were played between the National and American Leagues. The National League won 34 of them. What percent did the American League win?

   _____**35.8%**_____

Algebra © Scott, Foresman and Company   **39**

LESSON MASTER 5-5
QUESTIONS ON **SPUR** OBJECTIVES

■**REPRESENTATIONS**   *Objective J* (See pages 256–259 for objectives.)

1. Two squares are drawn inside the rectangle. If a point is selected at random, what is the probability that it lies in the shaded region?   _____**.85**_____

2. A 20-minute audio tape has four songs with times in minutes and seconds as follows: A, 4:30; B, 4:00; C, 5:30; D, 6:00. If the tape is started at any random position, what is the probability that it will be playing song A or C?   _____**.5**_____

3. The total area of the United States is 3,623,420 square miles. This includes 79,537 square miles of water. What is the probability that a satellite which falls at a random location in the U.S. will land in water?   _____**.022**_____

4. In the spinner, any position is equally likely. What is the probability that the spinner lands in region A or C? $\frac{60 + k}{360}$

5. A dart lands randomly on the crossword puzzle board. What is the probability that it will land in an unshaded square?   _____**.78**_____

6. The baseball foul lines form an angle of 90°. Suppose that a batter hits a ball with no control over its direction. What is the probability that the ball will go outside the foul lines? $\frac{3}{4}$

40   *Algebra* © Scott, Foresman and Company

LESSON MASTER 5–6
QUESTIONS ON **SPUR** OBJECTIVES

■**USES** *Objective H* (See pages 256–259 for objectives.)
1. Helene received a Christmas bonus of 1.5 times her weekly salary. If her weekly salary was W dollars, how much was her bonus?

1.5W dollars

2. After a period of growth, a crystal was 1.2 times its original length. If its new length was 6.4 mm long, what was the original length of the crystal?

about 5.3 mm

3. A blade of grass appears to be 2″ thick under a 250-power microscope. What is its actual thickness?

.008 in.

■**REPRESENTATIONS** *Objective M*
In 4 and 5, give the image of point P under a size change of magnitude 3.

4. $P(2, 4)$ ____ **(6, 12)**   **5.** $P(-5, -8)$ ____ **(-15, -24)**

In 6 and 7, give the image of point P under a size change of magnitude $-\frac{1}{2}$.

6. $P(-4, 1)$ ____ $\left(2, -\frac{1}{2}\right)$ **7.** $P(x, -y)$ ____ $\left(-\frac{x}{2}, \frac{y}{2}\right)$

8. Graph the image of the triangle *ABC* under a size change of magnitude 2.

9. Graph the image of the triangle *PQR* under a size change of $-\frac{2}{3}$.

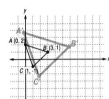

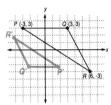

LESSON MASTER 5–7
QUESTIONS ON **SPUR** OBJECTIVES

■**SKILLS** *Objective C* (See pages 256–259 for objectives.)
In 1–8, solve.

1. $\frac{x}{40} = \frac{7}{8}$ **x = 35**   **2.** $\frac{-3}{5} = \frac{9}{y}$ **y = -15**

3. $\frac{7}{n} = 2.8$ **n = 2.5**   **4.** $\frac{3p}{-16} = \frac{21}{4}$ **p = -28**

5. $\frac{4k}{5} = -18$ $k = -\frac{45}{2}$ **6.** $\frac{1.8}{t} = \frac{4.2}{0.5}$ **t = .214**

7. $\frac{a}{\frac{1}{2}} = \frac{4}{\frac{1}{3}}$ **a = 6**   **8.** $\frac{-3.5}{0.4t} = \frac{-0.5}{6.6}$ **t = 115.5**

■**PROPERTIES** *Objective E*

9. If $\frac{p}{r} = \frac{2q}{3s}$, then by the Means-Extremes Property **3ps** = **2qr** .

10. If $\frac{3x}{5} = \frac{-2y}{7}$, then $\frac{7}{-2y} = $ $\frac{5}{3x}$.

■**USES** *Objective I*
11. Mr. Swenson can plow 3.5 acres in 1.5 hours. At that rate, how long would it take him to plow 10.5 acres?

4.5 hours

12. A certain recipe to serve 4 people calls for 280 grams of flour. How many grams of flour are needed if 7 people are to be served the same size portion?

490 grams

13. Anne earns $48 for each 100 envelopes she addresses. At that rate, how many envelopes will she have to address to earn $200?

417 envelopes

14. Ben used 8 gallons of gas to go 230 miles. Under the same driving conditions, how many gallons will he need to go 310 miles?

10.8 gallons

15. Jon used 2.5 gallons of paint to cover 900 square feet. How many gallons will he need to cover 1300 square feet?

3.61 gallons

LESSON MASTER 5–8
QUESTIONS ON **SPUR** OBJECTIVES

■**PROPERTIES** *Objective E* (See pages 256–259 for objectives.)
In 1–3, *x* and *y* are corresponding sides of similar figures. So are *a* and *b*.

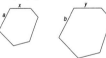

1. If $x = 4$, $y = 9$, and $a = 12$, then $b = $ __?__ .   **27**

2. If $x = 1.8$, $a = 0.6$, and $b = 1.1$, then $y = $ __?__ .   **3.3**

3. If $x = \frac{2}{3}$, $y = \frac{1}{2}$, and $b = \frac{3}{5}$, then $a = $ __?__ . $\frac{4}{5}$

4. What property must be used to answer 1–3?

The Means-Extremes Property

■**REPRESENTATIONS** *Objective K*
In 5–7, refer to the similar triangles. Corresponding sides are drawn with the same thickness.
5. Give one ratio of similitude.

$\frac{3}{4}$ or $\frac{4}{3}$

6. Find *x*.   **7.** Find *y*.

x = 6   **y = 10**

8. A surveyor made the measurements in the diagram to find the length of a pond. $\overline{PQ}$ is parallel to $\overline{RS}$. Find *RS*.

106 yards 2 feet

9. A building casts a shadow 51 feet long. At the same time, an 8-foot fence post casts a shadow 6 feet long. How high is the building?

68 feet

LESSON MASTER 6–1
QUESTIONS ON **SPUR** OBJECTIVES

■**SKILLS** *Objective B* (See pages 308–311 for objectives.)
In 1 and 2, solve and check.

1. $4y + 9 = -43$ **y = -13; 4(-13) + 9 = -43**

2. $62 = 5n - 13$ **n = 15; 62 = 5(15) - 13**

In 3–10, solve.

3. $13a - 72 = 58$ **4.** $6k + 23 = 17$ **5.** $3 + 2v = 17$

a = 10   **k = -1**   **v = 7**

6. $28 = 11w - 5$ **7.** $-8 = -8 + 4c$ **8.** $-2 = 13 + 3b$

w = 3   **c = 0**   **b = -5**

9. $6p - 16 = 23$ **10.** $-34 = 5t - 18$

p = 6.5 $t = -\frac{16}{5}$

■**PROPERTIES** *Objective D*
In 11–13, identify the property applied.

11. If $3x + 5 = 11$, then $3x = 6$.   **Add. Prop. of Equality**

12. If $2y + 18 = 12$ then $y + 9 = 6$.   **Mult. Prop. of Equality**

13. If $3t + 1 = 0$, then $6t + 2 = 0$.   **Mult. Prop. of Equality**

■**REPRESENTATIONS** *Objective J*
14. In the picture, the boxes are of equal weight and each cylinder weighs 1 kg.

a. Write an equation representing this situation.

2b + 3 = 7

b. What is the weight of one box? ____ **2 kg**

LESSON MASTER 6-2
QUESTIONS ON **SPUR** OBJECTIVES

■SKILLS *Objective B* (See pages 308–311 for objectives.)
In 1–8, solve.

1. $2s + 1.5 = 5.5$
$s = 2$

2. $11.7 + 5.6k = 25.7$
$k = 2.5$

3. $-0.7 = 0.8 + .3x$
$x = -5$

4. $\frac{5v}{12} - \frac{2}{3} = \frac{1}{6}$
$v = 2$

5. $5 + 7y - 3 = 37$
$y = 5$

6. $\frac{3}{4} = \frac{5}{8} + 2a$
$a = \frac{1}{16}$

7. $65 - 8x = 21$
$x = 5.5$

8. $\frac{7}{10} = 1 - \frac{3x}{5}$
$x = \frac{1}{2}$ or .0625

■USES *Objective H*

9. Freddie now weighs 260 pounds. To weigh 190 pounds in a half year (26 weeks), how much weight must he lose per week?

about 2.7 lb

10. At the U-Pick Strawberry Farm, Susan paid a total of $5.59 for the following: $.55 for an empty basket and $.48 a pound for the strawberries she picked. How many pounds of strawberries did she pick?

10.5 lb

11. Ms. Gower sells stereos. She gets a salary of $250 a week and a 5% commission on her total sales. If she earned a total of $400 one week, what was the total of her sales?

$3000

12. As air rises, it cools by expansion according to the formula $T = t - \frac{H}{100}$, where t is the Celsius temperature at the earth's surface, and T is the Celsius temperature at altitude H. If the air temperature at the surface is 25°C, how high must the balloon go to reach a height where the temperature is -5°?

3000 feet

LESSON MASTER 6-3
QUESTIONS ON **SPUR** OBJECTIVES

■SKILLS *Objective A* (See pages 308–311 for objectives.)
In 1–4, simplify.

1. $2x + x - 0.5x$ $2.5x$

2. $n - 0.25n$ $.75n$

3. $n + 0.06n + 10$ $1.06n + 10$

4. $6y + 4z - 3y$ $3y + 4z$

■PROPERTIES *Objectives D*
In 5 and 6, simplify using the Distributive Property.

5. $7(2a + 5)$ $14a + 35$

6. $x + x + 0.5x$ $2.5x$

■PROPERTIES *Objective E*
In 7–10, show how the Distributive Property can be used to perform the calculations mentally.

7. $4 \cdot \$9.95$ $4(10 - .05) = 40 - .2 = \$39.80$

8. $8 \cdot \$6.03$ $8(6 + .03) = 48 + .24 = \$48.24$

9. $202 \cdot 45$ $(200 + 2)45 = 9000 + 90 = 9090$

■USES *Objective F*
In 10–13, write and solve an equation for each question.

10. The Grossman's total dinner bill at a restaurant was $17.94. It included a 15% tip. What was the cost of the dinner before the tip?

$x + .15x = 17.94; x = \$15.60$

11. At some hotels, senior citizens get a 20% discount on a room. If the discounted price is $48 for a room, what is the regular price?

$x - .20x = 48; x = \$60$

■USES *Objective I*
12. Two angles are complementary. One is 4 times as large as the other. What are their measures?

$x + 4x = 90; x = 18°; 72°$

13. Peter opened a savings account that earns 6% in interest a year. He does not withdraw his money, and after a year, he has $402.80 in the account. Find the amount of his initial deposit.

$x + .06x = 402.80; x = \$380$

LESSON MASTER 6-4
QUESTIONS ON **SPUR** OBJECTIVES

■USES *Objective G* (See pages 308–311 for objectives.)
In 1–4, find the difference between two successive terms. Then give a formula for the nth term.

	Difference	nth term
1. 2, 5, 8, 11, . . .	3	$2 + 3(n - 1)$
2. 15, 11, 7, 3, . . .	-4	$15 - 4(n - 1)$
3. -1.3, -1.1, -0.9, . . .	.2	$-1.3 + .2(n - 1)$
4. $\frac{1}{4}, \frac{1}{2}, \frac{3}{4}, 1, . . .$	$\frac{1}{4}$	$\frac{1}{4}n$

5. In the sequence 3, 8, 13, 18, . . . , which term is 48?   **the 10th**

6. In the sequence 14.8, 14.5, 14.2, 13.9, . . . , which term is 11.8?   **the 11th**

7. In May, a store begins a closeout sale on coats by charging $34 per coat. The store reduces this price $5 per week until no coats remain. After how many weeks will remaining coats sell for $9 each?

5 weeks

8. A taxi company charges $1.10 for the first 0.1 mile, and $.10 for each additional 0.1 mile. If a trip costs a total of $2.60, how many miles is the trip?

1.5 miles

9. At 4 P.M. Jill must still drive 286 miles to reach her destination. She would like to stop for the night at 7 P.M. How fast must she drive to be 100 miles from her destination when she stops?

62 mph

10. In a certain bank, the minimum balance you must have in a checking account to avoid paying a service charge is $100. Ruth has a balance of $638. If she withdraws $48 a month for a car payment and makes no deposits, how many payments can she make without having a service charge?

11 payments

LESSON MASTER 6-5
QUESTIONS ON **SPUR** OBJECTIVES

■SKILLS *Objective B* (See pages 308–311 for objectives.)
In 1–8, solve.

1. $3a + 20 = -31$ $a = -17$

2. $-c + 4 = -24$ $c = 28$

3. $-72 - 18k = 18$ $k = -5$

4. $-1.3 - -1.1x = -0.9$ $x = \frac{4}{11}$ or $.36$

5. $\frac{1}{4}y + -\frac{1}{2} = \frac{3}{4}$ $y = 5$

6. $15d + 3d - 26d = -64$ $d = 8$

7. $.8m - 4.3m + 3.7m = -8.0$ $m = -40$

8. $\frac{1}{2}n + -\frac{5}{8}n = \frac{1}{4}n + \frac{7}{8}$ $n = -\frac{7}{8}$

9. The formula for finding the area of a triangle is $A = \frac{1}{2}bh$, where A is the area, b is the base, and h is the height. What is the height of a triangle that has a base of 3 cm and an area of 12 cm²?

h = 8 cm

10. In the sequence 3, 10, 17, 24, . . . , which term of the sequence is 52?

the 8th term

11. Not including the 7% sales tax, a sweater cost $28.42. How much did the sweater cost with tax?

$30.41

12. The Dennisons went to a Mexican restaurant and ordered tacos. Mr. Dennison ate twice as many tacos as Mrs. Dennison, and Greg Dennison ate three times as many tacos as his mother. If they ordered 12 tacos, how many did Greg eat?

6 tacos

13. A gallon of gasoline costs $1.02 at Bob's filling station. If you pay $11.67 to fill your tank completely, how many gallons of gasoline did you buy? Round to the nearest hundredth.

11.44 gallons

LESSON MASTER 6–6
QUESTIONS ON **SPUR** OBJECTIVES

■**SKILLS**   Objective B (See pages 308–311 for objectives.)
In 1–12, solve.

1. $n + 2 = 3n - 8$
$$n = 5$$

2. $6r - 7 = 3r - 22$
$$r = -5$$

3. $22 - 5a = 47 - 3a$
$$a = -\frac{25}{2}$$

4. $168 - 11t = 293 - 36t$
$$t = 5$$

5. $1.9 + 1.8x = 8.2x - 6.9$
$$x = 1.375$$

6. $.072v + .063 = .104v - .093$
$$v = 4.875$$

7. $\frac{2h}{3} + \frac{1}{2} = \frac{5h}{6} - \frac{3}{4}$
$$h = \frac{15}{2}$$

8. $\frac{9b}{5} - 3 = \frac{3b}{10} + 9$
$$b = 8$$

9. $\frac{p + 3}{4} = \frac{p - 1}{6}$
$$p = -11$$

10. $\frac{y - 8}{2} = \frac{y + 10}{5}$
$$y = 20$$

11. $2x + 7 - 3x = 4x + 9 - 3x$
$$x = -1$$

12. $16 - 3x - 9 = 28 - 2x + 4$
$$x = -25$$

■**PROPERTIES**   Objective D
In 13 and 14, identify the property being applied.

13. If $\frac{2}{A - 3} = \frac{3}{A + 1}$,
then $2A + 2 = 3A - 9$.   __Means-Extremes Property__

14. If $3x + a = -2x + 4a$,
then $5x = 3a$.   __Add. Prop. of Equality__

Algebra © Scott, Foresman and Company   Continued   **49**

LESSON MASTER 6–6
(page 2)

■**USES**   Objective G
15. A magician says, "I am thinking of a number. Twenty-one less than three times the number is five more than the number." Find the number.

_____ 13

16. A tank that contains 340 gallons of brine is being drained at a rate of 15 gallons per hour. Another tank which starts with 60 gallons is being filled at a rate of 20 gallons per hour. After how many hours will they both hold the same amount?

_____ 8 hours

■**USES**   Objective I
17. Janet has $105.00 and spends $5.00 every week. Marlene has $45.00 and saves $10.00 every week. In how many weeks will they have the same amount of money? **a.** Write an equation that describes this situation, and **b.** solve the problem.

a. __$105 - 5w = 45 + 10w$__

b. _____ 4 weeks

■**REPRESENTATIONS**   Objective J
In 18–20, the boxes in each picture are of equal weight. Every cylinder weighs one pound. For each question, a. write an equation in which B represents the weight of one box, and b. find the weight of one box.

18. a. __$2B + 9 = 5B + 3$__
b. __2 pounds__
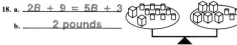

19. a. __$3B + 4 = B + 6$__
b. __1 pound__
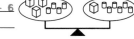

20. a. __$6B + 1 = 3B + 10$__
b. __3 pounds__

50   Algebra © Scott, Foresman and Company

LESSON MASTER 6–7
QUESTIONS ON **SPUR** OBJECTIVES

■**SKILLS**   Objective C (See pages 308–311 for objectives.)
In 1 and 2, solve and check.

1. $3a + 8 > 14$
$$a > 2$$

2. $19 > 7c - 2$
$$c < 3$$

In 3 and 4, solve and graph the solution on a number line.

3. $11 + 5n < -9$ $n < -4$
◄———————►

4. $23 \geq 17 + 6r$ $r \leq 1$
◄———————►

In 5–10, solve.

5. $19 - 4t > 3$
$$t < 4$$

6. $1.4 + 0.6y \leq 5.6$
$$y \leq 7$$

7. $\frac{2x}{3} - \frac{1}{2} > \frac{1}{3}$
$$x > \frac{5}{4}$$

8. $8u + 3 < 13u - 12$
$$u > 3$$

9. $6 \geq 9h - 15 - 2h$
$$h \leq 3$$

10. $5p + 3 - 2p \leq p$
$$p \leq -\frac{3}{2}$$

■**PROPERTIES**   Objective D
In 11 and 12, identify the property being used.

11. If $2x + 7 > x - 4$, then $x > -11$.

__Addition Property of Inequality__

12. If $-4x - 11 < 12$, then $4x + 11 > -12$.

__Multiplication Property of Inequality__

In 13 and 14, perform the indicated operation on both sides of the inequality.

13. $14a - 3 > 11 - 2a$; add $2a + 3$ to both sides.
_____ $16a > 14$

14. $31 - c < -4$; multiply both sides by -1.
_____ $-31 + c > 4$

Algebra © Scott, Foresman and Company   **51**

LESSON MASTER 6–8
QUESTIONS ON **SPUR** OBJECTIVES

■**SKILLS**   Objective A (See pages 308–311 for objectives.)
In 1–8, use the Distributive Property to eliminate the parentheses.

1. $2(3a + 2b)$ ____ $6a + 4b$

2. $4(3x - 5)$ ____ $12x - 20$

3. $0.06(20r + 50s)$ ____ $1.2r + 3s$

4. $1.12(7p - 4f)$ ____ $7.84p - 4.48f$

5. $\frac{2}{3}(9n - 6m)$ ____ $6n - 4m$

6. $\frac{5}{8}(12k + 16t)$ ____ $\frac{15}{2}k + 10t$

7. $4a(a + 23b + 17c)$ ____ $4a^2 + 92ab + 68ac$

8. $15uv(3v + 2y - 3)$ ____ $45uv^2 + 30uvy + -45uv$

In 9–12, simplify.

9. $4x + 3y + 2(x - 7y)$
____ $6x - 11y$

10. $9(a + 2b) - 3(2a - 5b)$
____ $3a + 33b$

11. $4f(6h - 2p + 1) + 2h(5f - 1)$
____ $34fh - 8fp + 4f - 2h$

12. $3(x + 2) + 8(6 - 2x - 3) - 9(5x + 9)$
____ $-58x - 51$

■**SKILLS**   Objective B
In 13–20, solve.

13. $3(2a - 5) = 15$
____ $a = 5$

14. $2(c + 7 + 3(c - 4)) = -3$
____ $c = \frac{7}{8}$

15. $4(y - 2) - 3(y + 7) = -34$
____ $y = -5$

16. $5(2x - 1) = 3(x + 3)$
____ $x = 2$

52   Continued   Algebra © Scott, Foresman and Company

LESSON MASTER 6-8
(page 2)

17. $\frac{1}{2}(6k + 3) = 4\frac{1}{2}$

$k = 1$

18. $\frac{2}{3}(n + 10) = \frac{3}{4}(n + 9)$

$n = -1$

19. $0.04(p + 1.1) = 0$

$p = -1.1$

20. $0.8(2p - 3) = 0.6(p - 4)$

$p = 0$

■**PROPERTIES** *Objective D*
In 21–23, identify the property being applied.

21. If $2x + 7y = -5x - y$, then $7x = -8y$.   **Add. Prop. of Equality**

22. $\frac{1}{2}(3 - 7x) = \frac{3}{2} - \frac{7x}{2}$ **Distributive Property**

23. If $3x = -8a$, then $x = \frac{-8a}{3}$.   **Mult. Prop. of Equality**

■**REPRESENTATIONS** *Objective J*
In 24–26, write two different expressions that describe the total area of the two rectangles.

24. $\dfrac{.2(.8 + .6) \text{ cm}^2}{(.16 + .12) \text{ cm}^2}$

25. $\dfrac{16(a + b) \text{ in.}^2}{(16a + 16b) \text{ in.}^2}$

26. $\dfrac{3(x + y) \text{ ft}^2}{(3x + 3y) \text{ ft}^2}$

LESSON MASTER 6-9
QUESTIONS ON **SPUR** OBJECTIVES

■**SKILLS** *Objective A (See pages 308–311 for objectives.)*
In 1–8, simplify.

1. $-(2x - 9)$

$-2x + 9$

2. $-(3a - 2b + 6c)$

$-3a + 2b - 6c$

3. $2 - (w + 4)$

$-w - 2$

4. $-(2a - 3) + (3a - 6)$

$a - 3$

5. $-3(4r + 3s) - (8r + s)$

$-20r - 10s$

6. $2.1d + 3.7 - (4.2d - 6.1)$

$-2.1d + 9.8$

7. $\frac{5m}{12} - \left(\frac{7m}{9} + 1\right)$

$-\frac{13}{36}m - 1$

8. $\frac{8k}{15} + \frac{7j}{30} - \left(\frac{7k}{15} + \frac{11j}{30}\right)$

$\frac{k}{15} - \frac{2j}{15}$

■**SKILLS** *Objective B*
In 9–12, solve.

9. $(8x - 3) - (5x + 6) = 6$

$x = 5$

10. $-(11x - 14) = -8$

$x = 2$

11. $2.6 = 1.8 - (0.2x - 1)$

$x = 1$

12. $7x - (2x + 1) = 7 - (x - 4)$

$x = 2$

■**PROPERTIES** *Objective D*
In 13 and 14, identify the property being applied.

13. If $12x + -4y = -15x - 3y$, then $27x = y$.   **Add. Prop. of Equality**

14. $-2(3 - 7x) = -6 + 14x$,   **Distributive Property**

LESSON MASTER 7-1
QUESTIONS ON **SPUR** OBJECTIVES

■**REPRESENTATIONS** *Objective H (See pages 360–363 for objectives.)*
In 1 and 2, a. make a table of values, b. graph the line, and
c. answer the question.

1. $y = 3x - 1$

a.

x	y
-1	-4
0	-1
1	2

b.

c. For what value of y will $(-2, y)$ be on the line?

$y = -7$

2. $y = 2 - x$

a.

x	y
-1	3
0	2
1	1

b.

c. For what value of x will $(x, 4)$ be on the line?

$x = -2$

3. Complete the chart for the graph.

x	y
-4	$\frac{1}{3}$
-3	0
-2	$\frac{1}{3}$
-1	$\frac{2}{3}$
0	1

4. *Multiple choice* Which equation describes the ordered pairs in the table below?

x	y
0	-8
1	-6
2	-4

(a) $y = x - 8$
(b) $y = 2x - 8$
(c) $y = -2x - 8$
(d) $y = 8 - 2x$

b

5. The difference d in dollars between the original price p of an item and its sale price of 14 dollars is given by $d = p - 14$. Complete the chart; then graph this relationship.

p	d
15	1
20	6
30	16

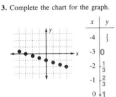

LESSON MASTER 7-2
QUESTIONS ON **SPUR** OBJECTIVES

■**REPRESENTATIONS** *Objective I (See pages 360–363 for objectives.)*
In 1–4, tell whether the statement is true or false.

1. The graph of $y = 6.1$ is a vertical line.   **false**

2. The graph of $x = 6$ is a horizontal line.   **false**

3. The boundary of the half plane satisfying $y > 4$ is a dotted line.   **true**

4. The boundary of the half plane satisfying $x \le -3.5$ is a solid line.   **true**

5. Graph the points in the plane satisfying $x > -1$.

6. Graph the points in the plane satisfying $y \le 2.5$.

In 7 and 8, give a sentence describing the shaded region.

7. $x > -4$

8. $y \ge 5$

9. Write an equation for the line containing $(3, 1)$ and $(3, 5)$.

$x = 3$

10. Paul weighed himself every day for a week. Each time he weighed 145 lb. Using w for weight, write an equation satisfying this situation.

$w = 145$

LESSON MASTER 7–3
QUESTIONS ON **SPUR** OBJECTIVES

■**SKILLS** *Objective A (See pages 360–363 for objectives.)*
In 1–6, simplify.

1. $|12 - 19|$ _____ 7   2. $|6 - 81|$ _____ 75

3. $|-219 - 31|$ __ 250 __   4. $|-7| + |-2|$ _____ 9

5. $|18| - |-12|$ _____ 6   6. $ABS(-1.8 + 0.6)$ _____ 1.2

■**REPRESENTATIONS** *Objective G*
In 7–12, find the distance on a number line between the points with the given coordinates.

7. 237 and 182 ___ 55 ___   8. 12 and -2 _____ 14

9. -32 and 14 ___ 46 ___   10. -0.64 and -0.42 ___ .22 ___

11. $-\frac{1}{2}$ and $-\frac{3}{4}$ _____ $\frac{1}{4}$ 12. r and -25 ___ $|r + 25|$ ___

13. Find the perimeter of the rectangle at right.
_____ 44 _____

(-6, 5)   (3, 5)
(-6, -8)   (3, -8)

14. The distance between two points on a number line with coordinates $8F - 3$ and $3F + 9$ is 15. Find all possible values of F. $\frac{27}{5}, -\frac{3}{5}$

■**REPRESENTATIONS** *Objective L*
In 15–18, find and graph all solutions.

15. $|x - 13| < 4$ $9 < x < 17$ 16. $|y + 9| = 1.5$ $y = -10.5$ or -7.5

(number line: 9 to 17)   (number line: -10.5, -7.5)

17. $|w - 4| > 8$ $-4 > w$ or $w > 12$ 18. $|y - 5| \le -2$ none

(number line: -4, 0, 12)   (number line y)

LESSON MASTER 7–4
QUESTIONS ON **SPUR** OBJECTIVES

■**SKILLS** *Objective B (See pages 360–363 for objectives.)*
In 1 and 2, a. approximate the square root to the nearest hundredth using your calculator. b. Show a check of your answer.

1. $\sqrt{1357}$ a. ___ 36.84 ___   2. $\sqrt{117}$ a. ___ 10.82 ___
   b. $(36.84)^2 = 1357.19$ b. $(10.82)^2 = 117.07$

In 3 and 4, find the two integers between which the square root lies.

3. $-\sqrt{87}$ __ -10 __ and __ -9 __   4. $\sqrt{103}$ __ 10 __ and __ 11 __

In 5–12, simplify.

5. $\sqrt{9 + 16}$ 6. $\sqrt{4 \cdot 9}$ 7. $\sqrt{9} + \sqrt{16}$
     5   6   7

8. $\sqrt{4} \cdot \sqrt{9}$ 9. $2 + \sqrt{\frac{18}{2}}$ 10. $7 - \sqrt{\frac{75}{3}}$
     6   5   2

11. $5\sqrt{8} \cdot \sqrt{8}$ 12. $-4\sqrt{13} \cdot \sqrt{13}$
     40   -52

13. Evaluate $35 - \sqrt{1 + 4n}$ when $n = 30$. ___ 24 ___

14. Evaluate $4(7 + 2\sqrt{x})$ when $x = 25$. ___ 68 ___

15. Evaluate $3(\sqrt{x})^2$ when $x = 3$. ___ 9 ___

■**SKILLS** *Objective C*
In 16–23, solve. Give the exact answer in simplified form.

16. $11n^2 = 187$ $n = \sqrt{17}$ or $-\sqrt{17}$ 17. $-2a^2 = 32$ no solution

18. $\frac{7}{m} = \frac{m}{5}$ $m = \sqrt{35}$ or $-\sqrt{35}$ 19. $\frac{k}{7} = \frac{13}{k}$ $k = \sqrt{91}$ or $-\sqrt{91}$

20. $\sqrt{y} - 9 = 25$ $y = 1156$ 21. $4\sqrt{t} + 7 = 35$ $t = 49$

22. $2x^2 - 28 = 100$ $x = 8$ or -8 23. $3y^2 + 10 = 157$ $y = 7$ or -7

■**USES** *Objective F*
24. A side of a square is $5\sqrt{13}$ cm. Find the area of the square.   325 cm²

25. Four square tiles fit together to cover an area of 324 sq in. Find the length of the side of one tile.   9 in.

LESSON MASTER 7–5
QUESTIONS ON **SPUR** OBJECTIVES

■**USES** *Objective F (See pages 360–363 for objectives.)*

1. A carpenter designs a brace for the corner of a frame as shown. Find the length c of the brace.

c, 4 ft, 3 ft

_____ 5 feet _____

2. A suitcase is 80 cm long and 50 cm wide. What is the length of the largest umbrella that can fit in the suitcase?   ___ about 94 cm ___

3. Two boats leave a dock at the same time. One sails north at 9 mph, the other sails east at 10 mph. How far apart are they after 2 hours?

9 mph, 10 mph

___ about 27 miles ___

4. Suppose you wanted to construct a ski lift that rises 50 m and extends a horizontal distance of 120 m. Ignoring the slack in the cable, what distance would the cable extend?

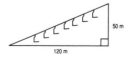
50 m, 120 m

_____ 130 m _____

LESSON MASTER 7–5
(page 2)

■**REPRESENTATIONS** *Objective J*

5. Examine the right triangle at the right.

v, t, u

   a. What variables represent the lengths of the legs?
   _____ *v and t* _____

   b. What variable represents the length of the hypotenuse?
   _____ *u* _____

6. Find the value of c in the triangle at the right.

c, 12, 35

_____ 37 _____

7. Find the value of a in the triangle at the right.

18, a, 23

_____ $\sqrt{205}$ _____

8. Find the length of the hypotenuse of the triangle at the right.

6.3, 8.4

_____ 10.5 _____

9. The diagonal of a rectangle is 26 and one side is 10. Find the lengths of all other sides.
   ___ 24 ___   ___ 10 ___   ___ 24 ___

10. The diagonal of a square is $5\sqrt{2}$. Find the length of each side of the square.
   _____ 5 _____

LESSON **MASTER** 7-6
QUESTIONS ON **SPUR** OBJECTIVES

■SKILLS *Objective B (See pages 360–363 for objectives.)*
In 1–4, simplify. Use your calculator to check your answer.

1. $\sqrt{32}$ $4\sqrt{2}$ 2. $\sqrt{27}$ $3\sqrt{3}$

3. $\sqrt{108}$ $6\sqrt{3}$ 4. $\sqrt{147}$ $7\sqrt{3}$

5. Evaluate $\sqrt{3 + 23n}$ when $n = 3$. $6\sqrt{2}$

6. Evaluate $\sqrt{64 - 7n}$ when $n = 2$. $5\sqrt{2}$

■PROPERTIES *Objective E*
In 7 and 8, solve. Simplify your answer.

7. $2x^2 = 24$ $x = \pm 2\sqrt{3}$ 8. $\frac{14}{m} = \frac{m}{7}$ $m = \pm 7\sqrt{2}$

In 9–16, simplify.

9. $\sqrt{25 + 25}$ $5\sqrt{2}$

10. $\sqrt{72 + 72}$ 12

11. $2\sqrt{48}$ $8\sqrt{3}$

12. $3\sqrt{200}$ $30\sqrt{2}$

13. $\frac{\sqrt{52}}{2}$ $\sqrt{13}$

14. $\frac{\sqrt{135}}{6}$ $\frac{\sqrt{15}}{2}$

15. $\sqrt{12} \cdot \sqrt{3} + \sqrt{8} \cdot \sqrt{2}$ 10

16. $\sqrt{50} \cdot \sqrt{8} - \sqrt{18} \cdot \sqrt{2}$ 14

In 17 and 18, simplify. Assume all variables are positive.

17. $\sqrt{25a^2b^3}$ $5ab$ 18. $\sqrt{81x^2y^2}$ $9xy$

■USES *Objective F*
19. Each side of a square is 9. Find the diagonal and simplify your answer. $9\sqrt{2}$

20. The sides of a rectangle are 6 and 15. Find the diagonal and simplify your answer. $3\sqrt{29}$

LESSON **MASTER** 7-7
QUESTIONS ON **SPUR** OBJECTIVES

■REPRESENTATIONS *Objective K (See pages 360–363 for objectives.)*
In 1–6, use the graph at the right. The midpoint of AC is M. Determine each length.

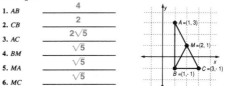

1. AB 4
2. CB 2
3. AC $2\sqrt{5}$
4. BM $\sqrt{5}$
5. MA $\sqrt{5}$
6. MC $\sqrt{5}$

In 7–10, find XY.

7. $X = (4, 9)$ and $Y = (1, 5)$ 5

8. $X = (-3, 6)$ and $Y = (2, -6)$ 13

9. $X = (-11, -16)$ and $Y = (0, -20)$ $\sqrt{137}$

10. $X = (1.8, -2.4)$ and $Y = (1.2, -1.6)$ 1

In 11 and 12, use the diagram at the right. Each small square represents a city block.

11. What is the street distance between R and N? 8 blocks

12. How far is it from R to N as the crow flies? $\sqrt{34}$ or about 5.8 blocks

In 13–15, use the graph of the rectangle.

13. Find OB. $\sqrt{a^2 + b^2}$

14. Find AC. $\sqrt{a^2 + b^2}$

15. What can you conclude about the diagonals of a rectangle?   They are equal in length.

LESSON **MASTER** 7-8
QUESTIONS ON **SPUR** OBJECTIVES

■SKILLS *Objective D (See pages 360–363 for objectives.)*

1. If $4y = 5.1$, find $12y$. 15.3
2. If $3n + 1 = 11$, find $9n + 3$. 33
3. If $2x^2 = 9$, find $(2x^2)^2$. 81
4. If $\sqrt{5p - 1} = 7$, find $5p - 1$. 49
5. If $8k = 15$, find $16k - 1$. 29
6. If $-6s = 19$, find $12s + 5$. -33
7. If $3t + 6u = -3$, and $2u = -3$, find $3t$. 6
8. If $4f - 8g = 9$, and $2g = 1$, find $4f$. 13

In 9–12, simplify.

9. $7\sqrt{3} + 4\sqrt{3} - 6\sqrt{3} - 3\sqrt{3}$ $2\sqrt{3}$

10. $4\sqrt{w + 5} + 13\sqrt{w + 5} - \sqrt{w + 5}$ $16\sqrt{w + 5}$

11. $12(x - 4) - 17(x - 4) - 2(x - 4)$ $-7(x - 4)$

12. $5(2y - 1)^2 - 8(2y - 1)^2 + 3(2y - 1)^2$ 0

In 13–20, solve.

13. $(t + 3)^2 = 9$ $t = 0$ or -6

14. $(d - 4)^2 = 49$ $d = 11$ or -3

15. $\sqrt{3y - 2} = 5$ $y = 9$

16. $\sqrt{4p + 5} = 9$ $p = 19$

17. $|3w + 7| = 22$ $w = 5$ or $\frac{-29}{3}$

18. $|11q - 4| = 29$ $q = 3$ or $\frac{-25}{11}$

19. $\frac{x + 1}{2} = \frac{8}{x + 1}$ $x = 3$ or -5

20. $\frac{9}{3x - 3} = \frac{3x - 3}{4}$ $x = 3$ or -1

LESSON **MASTER** 8-1
QUESTIONS ON **SPUR** OBJECTIVES

■USES *Objective G (See pages 418–421 for objectives.)*
In 1–4, use the data given below on number of deaths in the U.S. caused by home fires.

Year	No. Deaths	Year	No. Deaths
1950	5000	1970	5600
1955	5400	1975	5000
1960	6350	1980	4400
1965	6100		

1. Graph the situation on the axes below.

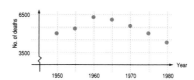

2. Find the rate of change of deaths per year from 1950 to 1955.   80 deaths per year

3. a. In which five-year period did the number of deaths increase the most?   1955–1960

   b. What was the rate of change of deaths per year for that period?   190 deaths per year

4. a. In which two five-year periods was the rate of change the same?   1970–1975, 1975–1980

   b. What was the average rate of change of deaths per year in those periods?   -120 deaths per year

5. Using only the trend shown by the data for 1960–1980, predict an estimate for the number of deaths in the U.S. caused by home fires in 1985.   about 4000

LESSON MASTER 8-2
QUESTIONS ON **SPUR** OBJECTIVES

■**SKILLS** *Objective A* (See pages 418–421 for objectives.)
In 1–4, find the slope of the line through the given points.

1. (2, -4), (5, -1)

1

2. (12, 3), (2, 7)

$-\frac{2}{5}$

3. (-5.2, 3.7), (7.2, 4.1)

$\frac{1}{31}$

4. (4, k), (-2, k)

0

5. Determine whether the points (3, -1), (5, 2), (9, 8) lie on the same line. If they do, give the slope of that line.

yes, $\frac{3}{2}$

■**PROPERTIES** *Objective D*

6. If the slope of a line is $\frac{?}{}$, then as x increases, y decreases.

negative

7. Consider lines ℓ, m, and n graphed at right.
  a. Which line has slope -2?

  n

  b. Which line has slope $-\frac{1}{3}$?

  m

  c. Which line has slope 0?

  ℓ

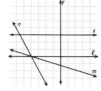

■**PROPERTIES** *Objective F*
In 8–10, find the slope of the line with the given equation.

8. $2x + y = 6$

-2

9. $5x - 2y = 10$

$\frac{5}{2}$

10. $x = 8$

no slope

■**REPRESENTATIONS** *Objective I*
11. Graph the line which passes through (0, 1) and has a slope of -2.

Algebra © Scott, Foresman and Company

65

LESSON MASTER 8-3
QUESTIONS ON **SPUR** OBJECTIVES

■**PROPERTIES** *Objective D* (See pages 418–421 for objectives.)
1. Why does the line through (4, 1) and (4, -2) not have a slope?

The slope of a vertical
line is undefined.

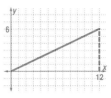

■**REPRESENTATIONS** *Objective I*
2. A roof rises 6 inches for each 12 inches of horizontal distance. Calculate the slope of this roof and picture it at right.

$\frac{1}{2}$

In 3–6, graph the line passing through the given point and having the given slope.

3. (-2, 1), slope $\frac{1}{2}$

4. (4, 2), slope -2

5. (-1, -3), slope $\frac{1}{3}$

6. (0, -2), slope $-\frac{2}{3}$

7. Name one other point on the line through (-5, 2) with slope 2.

sample: (-4, 4)

8. Name one other point on the line through (0, $-\frac{1}{2}$) with slope $\frac{3}{2}$.

sample: (1, 1)

66

Algebra © Scott, Foresman and Company

LESSON MASTER 8-4
QUESTIONS ON **SPUR** OBJECTIVES

■**SKILLS** *Objective B* (See pages 418–421 for objectives.)
In 1–4, write an equation for the line with the given slope m and y-intercept b.

1. $m = 3$, $b = -1$

$y = 3x - 1$

2. $m = 11.2$, $b = -3.9$

$y = 11.2x - 3.9$

3. $m = -3.2$, $b = 0$

$y = -3.2x$

4. $m = 4$, $b = p$

$y = 4x + p$

■**PROPERTIES** *Objective E*
In 5–8, write each equation in slope-intercept form.

5. $8x = 13 - 2y$

$y = -4x + \frac{13}{2}$

6. $5x + 3y = -2$

$y = -\frac{5}{3}x - \frac{2}{3}$

7. $x - y = 2$

$y = x - 2$

8. $y = 5$

$y = 0x + 5$

■**PROPERTIES** *Objective F*
In 9–11, find the slope and the y-intercept of the given line.

9. $y = -2$ slope ____0____ y-intercept ___-2___

10. $2x - 8y = 11$ slope ___$\frac{1}{4}$___ y-intercept ___$-\frac{11}{8}$___

11. $x = 23$ slope __undefined__ y-intercept ___none___

■**USES** *Objective H*
12. For an increase of one Kelvin (K), the Fahrenheit temperature (F) goes up 1.8 degrees. If $F = 32°$ when $K = 273.15$, write an equation for F in terms of K.

$F = 1.8K - 459.67$

■**REPRESENTATIONS** *Objective I*
13. Graph the line which passes through (-2,4) and has a slope of -2.

Algebra © Scott, Foresman and Company

67

LESSON MASTER 8-5
QUESTIONS ON **SPUR** OBJECTIVES

■**SKILLS** *Objective B* (See pages 418–421 for objectives.)
In 1–8, given one point and slope, find an equation for the line.

1. point (4, -4), slope -3

$y = -3x + 8$

2. point (-3, 1), slope $\frac{2}{3}$

$y = \frac{2}{3}x + 3$

3. point (2.5, 6), slope 0.8

$y = .8x + 4$

4. point (-15, 0), slope $-\frac{3}{5}$

$y = -\frac{3}{5}x - 9$

5. point (5, -9), slope 0

$y = -9$

6. point (5, 8), slope undefined

$x = 5$

7. point (0, $\frac{1}{2}$), slope $-\frac{1}{8}$

$2x + 16y = 8$

8. point (0, -3), slope 4

$12x - 3y = 9$

■**USES** *Objective H*
9. A repairperson charges $25 per hour plus an initial service-call charge. The bill for 3 hours was $105. Give a linear equation which relates the cost y of having the repairperson work x hours.

$y = 25x + 30$

10. Rich Nomore has been spending 65 cents on bus fare each day from a coin wallet. After 12 days, he has $4.70 left. Write an equation giving the amount y he had left after x days.

$y = -.65x + 12.50$

11. It costs $1.25 for a 3-minute call and 30¢ for each additional minute. Give the cost c for a m-minute call, when $m > 3$.

$c = .30(m - 3) + 1.25$

12. There are 100 days gone of the school year and 40,000 sheets of duplicating paper are left. If about 2,000 sheets are used each day, how many sheets s were left after d days of school?

$s = -2000d + 240,000$

68

Algebra © Scott, Foresman and Company

LESSON MASTER 8-6
QUESTIONS ON SPUR OBJECTIVES

■SKILLS *Objective C (See pages 418–421 for objectives.)*
In 1–6, find an equation for the line through the two given points.

1. (4, -1), (7, 5)

$y = 2x - 9$

2. (204, 358), (300, 406)

$y = \frac{1}{2}x + 256$

3. (-0.43, 1.8), (0.57, -3.6)

$y = -5.4x - .522$

4. $\left(\frac{2}{3}, \frac{3}{2}\right), \left(\frac{5}{6}, \frac{3}{4}\right)$

$y = -\frac{9}{2}x + \frac{9}{2}$

5. (0, 0), (1, $\sqrt{2}$)

$y = \sqrt{2}x$

6. (a, 0), (0, b)

$y = -\frac{b}{a}x + b$

7. a. Find an equation for the line through (-3, -8) and (1, 1).

$y = \frac{9}{4}x - \frac{5}{4}$

b. Does the point (9, 19) lie on the line?

yes

■USES *Objective H*

8. A linear equation can be used to describe the length of a spring, y, when it is stretched by a weight, x. A spring is 4 cm long when a 50-g weight is attached, and 6 cm long when a 74-g weight is attached. Write an equation which relates x and y.

$y = \frac{1}{12}x - \frac{1}{6}$

9. A man whose foot is 12 in. long wears a size 12 shoe. A man whose foot is 10 in. long wears a size 6 shoe. If the shoe size, S, and the foot length, F, are linearly related, write an equation which describes that relation.

$S = 3F - 24$

10. a. Harvey began his diet when he weighed 260 pounds. After four weeks he weighed 246 pounds. If he lost weight at a constant rate, write an equation which relates his weight, W, and the number of weeks on the diet, n.

$W = 260 - 3.5n$

b. Why doesn't this relation work when n is large?

He would eventually have no weight or negative weight.

LESSON MASTER 8-7
QUESTIONS ON SPUR OBJECTIVES

■REPRESENTATIONS *Objective J (See pages 418–421 for objectives.)*
1. Below is a table showing the median height in cm of boys in the U.S. by age.

Age	Height (cm)	Age	Height (cm)	Age	Height (cm)
2	87	8	127	14	163
3	95	9	132	15	169
4	103	10	138	16	174
5	110	11	143	17	176
6	116	12	150	18	177
7	122	13	160		

a. Graph this data, and sketch a line to fit the data.

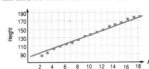

b. Find an equation for the line. sample: $H = 6A + 80$

2. The table below gives the life expectancy of the average person at birth in the U.S. for the years 1900–1980.

Year	Expectancy	Year	Expectancy
1900	47.3	1950	68.2
1910	50.0	1960	69.7
1920	54.1	1970	70.8
1930	59.7	1980	73.8
1940	62.9		

a. Graph this data, and sketch a line to fit the data.

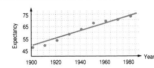

b. Find an equation for the line. sample: $E = .28y - 481$

c. What life expectancy would you predict in 1990? about 76 years

---

LESSON MASTER 8-8
QUESTIONS ON SPUR OBJECTIVES

■PROPERTIES *Objective E (See pages 418–421 for objectives.)*
In 1–6, rewrite the equation in slope-intercept form.

1. $5x + 2y = 10$

$y = -\frac{5}{2}x + 5$

2. $6x = 16 - 3y$

$y = -2x + \frac{16}{3}$

3. $-15x + 7y = 14$

$y = \frac{15}{7}x + 2$

4. $-7x = 6 - 13y$

$y = \frac{7}{13}x + \frac{6}{13}$

5. $2x + y = -6$

$y = -2x - 6$

6. $12x = -15 - 3y$

$y = -4x - 5$

In 7–12, rewrite the equation in standard form with integer coefficients.

7. $1.1x = .2y + 9$

$11x - 2y = 90$

8. $0.6y = 0.7x - 2$

$7x - 6y = 20$

9. $\frac{2}{3}x - \frac{3}{4}y - 1 = 0$

$8x - 9y = 12$

10. $y = -\frac{4}{3}x - 1$

$4x + 3y = -3$

11. $5.5x - 3y = 1.0$

$11x - 6y = 2$

12. $0.6x = 1.6 - 5.3y$

$6x + 53y = 16$

■USES *Objective H*
13. Tickets for the concert are $6 and $4. If s six-dollar tickets and f four-dollar tickets were sold and $1000 was taken in, **a.** give a possible pair of values of s and f and **b.** write an equation relating s and f.

a. sample: $s = 50$, $f = 175$ **b.** $6s + 4f = 1000$

14. Paula worked for x hours at $4 an hour and y hours at time and a half. She earned a total of $48. Write an equation that relates x and y.

$4x + 6y = 48$

LESSON MASTER 8-9
QUESTIONS ON SPUR OBJECTIVES

■REPRESENTATIONS *Objective K (See pages 418–421 for objectives.)*
In 1–6, graph the inequality.

1. $y \geq 2x - 3$

2. $y < -\frac{x}{2} + 1$

3. $4x - 3y < 6$

4. $2x - 6y \geq 0$

5. $5x + 3y \leq 0$

6. $y - 3 < 0$

In 7 and 8, **a.** write an inequality to fit each situation, and **b.** draw the graph.

7. For a performance, adult tickets are $5 and children's tickets are $3. To make a profit, at least $2000 must be collected. The ticket sales were a adult and c children's tickets.

a. $5a + 3c \geq 2000$

b.

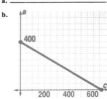

8. Henry plans to buy x 25-cent stamps and y 20-cent stamps. He has $7.50 to spend, but does not need to spend all of it.

a. $25x + 20y \leq 750$

b.

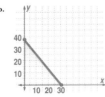

LESSON MASTER 9–1
QUESTIONS ON **SPUR** OBJECTIVES

■**USES** *Objective F (See pages 471–473 for objectives.)*
In 1–4, find the amount for each of the following bank accounts after one year for the given principal and annual yield.

1. $100, 5.5%
$105.50

2. $240, 6%
$254.40

3. $1200, 7.5%
$1290.00

4. $2500, 8.4%
$2710.00

5. Suppose P dollars is invested in a Certificate of Deposit (CD) with an annual yield of 7.2% for 3 years. Write an expression for the amount received when the CD matures.
1.23P

6. Petra opened a savings account by depositing $800. If the annual yield is 5.8%, write an expression for the amount in the account after n years.
$800(1.058)^n

In 7 and 8, find the amount in an account from the given information.

7. $400 at 5.7% after 3 years
$472.37

8. $2200 at 7.8% after 2 years
$2556.58

In 9 and 10, find the interest earned from the given information.

9. $180 at 5% for 2 years
$18.45

10. $1 at 6% for 4 years
$.26

11. a. Which will earn more interest, $120 at 4% for 2 years or $120 at 8% for 1 year?
$120 at 4% for 2 yr

b. By how much do the earnings differ?
by 19 cents

12. If $200 is deposited in an account with an annual yield of 10%, in how many years will the amount double?
a little over 7 yr

13. In 1626, Peter Minuit bought Manhattan Island from the Manhattan Indians for beads, clothing, and trinkets worth about $24. If that money had been invested at 5% annual yield, what would the amount be in 1988?
about $1,240,000,000

Algebra © Scott, Foresman and Company   **73**

LESSON MASTER 9–2
QUESTIONS ON **SPUR** OBJECTIVES

■**SKILLS** *Objective A (See pages 471–473 for objectives.)*
In 1–9, evaluate.

1. 2^4 ___ **16**

2. -2^4 ___ **-16**

3. $(-2)^4$ ___ **16**

4. $4 \cdot 17^0$ ___ **4**

5. -5^3 ___ **-125**

6. $(-5)^3$ ___ **-125**

7. If $x = -4$, then $10 + x^0 = $ ___ **11** .

8. $3 \cdot 10^2 + 6 \cdot 10^1 + 8 \cdot 10^0$ ___ **368**

9. $8 \cdot 10^0 + 2 \cdot 10^1 + 1 \cdot 10^2$ ___ **128**

■**PROPERTIES** *Objective E*
In 10 and 11, tell whether the statement is true or false. If false, correct the statement by changing the right side of the equation.

10. $12 + x^0 = 12$
false; $12 + x^0 = 13$

11. If $x = 3$ and $y = 2$, then $(x + y)^0 = 1$.
true

■**USES** *Objective G*
12. Suppose that 10 squirrels are introduced to an area. If their population doubles every three months, how many squirrels are there in 1 year?
160 squirrels

13. The number of people who ride skateboards in a town is growing at the rate of 20% per year. If 400 ride skateboards now and the growth rate remains constant, how many will ride skateboards in 3 years?
691 people

14. A gray filter lets in only $\frac{2}{5}$ of the light that hits it. What fraction (or portion) of the light would pass through a series of 3 of these filters?
$\frac{8}{125}$ of light

15. A copy machine can make an enlargement 1.2 times as large as the original. If you make copies of copies, enlarging each time, how many times as large as the original will the fourth copy be?
about 2.1 times as large

74   *Algebra © Scott, Foresman and Company*

LESSON MASTER 9–3
QUESTIONS ON **SPUR** OBJECTIVES

■**USES** *Objective G (See pages 471–473 for objectives.)*

1. A 6″ by 4″ drawing is reduced three times by using a photocopy machine. Each time it is reduced to 90% of its previous dimensions. What is its final size?
≈4.4″ by 2.9″

2. Suppose a radioactive substance loses $\frac{1}{2}$ of its remaining mass each second. How much of a 36 g sample will remain after 6 seconds?
0.5625 g

3. Each year an automobile depreciates in value by 25%. Find the value after five years of a car which cost $4800 new.
$1139.06

4. Because of the use of an antibiotic, 15% of the bacteria die each hour. After how many hours will less than 50% of the original bacteria remain alive?
5 hours

5. The population of a large city has been decreasing 2% each year. At this rate, what will be the percent of loss in a decade?
≈18.3% less

6. The enrollment at a certain college is increasing at the rate of 2% per year. If there are presently 1752 students, how many will there be in 10 years?
2136 students

Algebra © Scott, Foresman and Company   **75**

LESSON MASTER 9–4
QUESTIONS ON **SPUR** OBJECTIVES

■**REPRESENTATIONS** *Objective I (See pages 471–473 for objectives.)*
In 1–4, tell whether the graph of each equation is linear or exponential.

1. $y = 2x + 5$
linear

2. $y = 20 - .06x$
linear

3. $y = 20(.06)^x$
exponential

4. $y = 2(1.05)^x$
exponential

5. When x is large and increases, for which equation does y increase more rapidly?

(a) $y = 24 + 6x$ (b) $y = 24(1.06)^x$
b

In 6–9, match each equation with its graph.

6. $y = 10 - 5x$ **d**

7. $y = 10(1.5)^x$ **a**

8. $y = 10 + 5x$ **b**

9. $y = 10(0.5)^x$ **c**

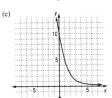
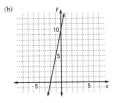
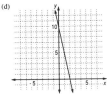

76 *Continued*   *Algebra © Scott, Foresman and Company*

LESSON MASTER 9-4
(page 2)

In 10 and 11, graph.

10. $y = 3^x$ for $-3 \le x \le 3$

11. $y = 0.5^x$ for $-3 \le x \le 3$

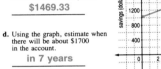

12. $1000 is invested in a savings account at an 8% annual yield.

a. Complete the table below for the amount in the account after 0, 2, 4, 6, and 8 years.

Year	0	2	4	6	8
Amount Saved	$1000	$1166.40	$1360.49	$1586.87	$1850.93

b. Graph the situation.

c. Approximately how much is in the account after 5 years?

$1469.33

d. Using the graph, estimate when there will be about $1700 in the account.

in 7 years

LESSON MASTER 9-5
QUESTIONS ON **SPUR** OBJECTIVES

■**SKILLS** *Objective A (See pages 471–473 for objectives.)*

1. Evaluate $3^2 \cdot 3^3$. **243**
2. Evaluate $(3^2)^3$. **729**

3. Find the value of $x^3 \cdot x^4$ when $x = 2$. **128**

4. Find the value of $(2y)^5$ when $y = -1$. **-32**

■**SKILLS** *Objective B*
In 5–18, simplify.

5. $a^5 \cdot a^7$ **a^{12}**
6. $2n^0 \cdot n^8$ **$2n^8$**

7. $6t^6 \cdot 3t^2$ **$18t^8$**
8. $0.7b^3 \cdot 0.4b^9$ **$0.28b^{12}$**

9. $u^7 \cdot v^2 \cdot u^6 \cdot v^4$ **$u^{13}v^6$**
10. $g^5 \cdot k^3 \cdot g^8 \cdot k^9$ **$g^{13}k^{12}$**

11. $(b^6c^5)(b^2c^6)$ **b^8c^{11}**
12. $(w^5)^2$ **w^{10}**

13. $3(h^4)^3$ **$3h^{12}$**
14. $(3h^4)^3$ **$27h^{12}$**

15. $(x^4)^2(x^4)^2$ **x^{16}**
16. $(x^2)^4 + (x^4)^2$ **$2x^8$**

17. $(a + b)^4(a + b)^5$ **$(a + b)^9$**
18. $(2s - 3t)^3(2s - 3t)^8$ **$(2s - 3t)^{11}$**

■**PROPERTIES** *Objective E*
In 19–22, name the property or properties which justify each statement.

19. $r^9r^6 = r^{15}$ **Product of Powers Property**

20. $(4d^3)d^2 = 4d^5$ **Associative Property of Multiplication and Product of Powers Property**

21. $(a^8)^4 = a^{32}$ **Power of a Power Property**

In 22–25, tell whether the statement is true or false. If false, correct the statement by changing the right side of the equation.

22. $(p^3)^4 = p^7$ **false; $(p^3)^4 = p^{12}$**
23. $q^5 \cdot q^3 = q^8$ **true**

24. $(5^3)^0 = 0$ **false; $(5^3)^0 = 1$**
25. $3x^2 \cdot 2x^3 = 5x^5$ **false; $3x^2 \cdot 2x^3 = 6x^5$**

LESSON MASTER 9-6
QUESTIONS ON **SPUR** OBJECTIVES

■**SKILLS** *Objective A (See pages 471–473 for objectives.)*
In 1–6, evaluate.

1. 5^{-1} **$\frac{1}{5}$**
2. 10^{-4} **$\frac{1}{10,000}$**
3. $7 \cdot 4^{-3}$ **$\frac{7}{64}$**

4. $-9 \cdot 3^{-3}$ **$-\frac{1}{3}$**
5. -2^{-6} **$\frac{1}{64}$**
6. $(-2)^{-6}$ **$\frac{1}{64}$**

In 7–10, simplify.

7. $3 \cdot 10^1 + 1 \cdot 10^0 + 4 \cdot 10^{-1}$ **31.4**

8. $7 \cdot 10^0 + 2 \cdot 10^{-1} + 6 \cdot 10^{-3}$ **7.206**

9. $8 \cdot 10^4 + 5 \cdot 10^0 + 9 \cdot 10^{-1}$ **80,005.9**

10. $8^{17} \cdot 8^{-17}$ **1**

■**SKILLS** *Objective B*
In 11–18, rewrite without a negative exponent.

11. xy^3 **$\frac{x}{y^{-3}}$**
12. $2a^{-4}$ **$\frac{2}{a^4}$**
13. $3t^{-5}$ **$\frac{3}{t^5}$**

14. $(b^7)^{-2}$ **$\frac{1}{b^{14}}$**
15. $(4y)^{-1}$ **$\frac{1}{4y}$**
16. m^6n^{-3} **$\frac{m^6}{n^3}$**

17. $a^3b^{-2}c^4$ **$\frac{a^3c^4}{b^2}$**
18. $w^{-6}x^2y^{-5}$ **$\frac{x^2}{w^6y^5}$**

■**PROPERTIES** *Objective E*
In 19 and 20, name the property or properties which justify each statement.

19. $x^5y^{-1} = \frac{x^5}{y}$ **Negative Exponent Property**

20. $(a^3)^{-2} = \frac{1}{a^6}$ **Power of a Power and Negative Exponent Properties**

■**USES** *Objective H*
21. The population of a town is 25,194. It has been gaining 8% for each of the last three years. What was the population three years ago? **20,000 people**

22. Hakeem has $2917 in a Certificate of Deposit which has an annual yield of 5%. How much was it worth 4 years ago? **$2399.82**

LESSON MASTER 9-7
QUESTIONS ON **SPUR** OBJECTIVES

■**SKILLS** *Objective A (See pages 471–473 for objectives.)*
In 1–6, evaluate.

1. $\frac{3^5}{3^8}$ **$\frac{1}{27}$**
2. $\frac{7^{12}}{7^8}$ **7^4**

3. $\frac{2^x}{2^x}$ **1**
4. $\frac{6^8}{6^9}$ **6**

5. $\frac{5.6 \cdot 10^{15}}{3.2 \cdot 10^{10}}$ **$1.75 \cdot 10^5$**
6. $\frac{1.21 \cdot 10^6}{8.8 \cdot 10^9}$ **$1.375 \cdot 10^{-4}$**

7. Rewrite $\frac{2187}{27} = 81$ using positive powers of 3. **$\frac{3^7}{3^3} = 3^4$**

■**SKILLS** *Objective B*
In 8–17, simplify.

8. $\frac{8a^9b^3}{2a^4b^2}$ **$4a^4b$**
9. $\frac{15r^4s}{25r^3s^3} \cdot r^3$ **$\frac{3r^5}{5s^4}$**

10. $\frac{(h + 2k)^5}{(h + 2k)^2}$ **$(h + 2k)^3$**
11. $\frac{(y - 8)^6}{(y - 8)^8}$ **$\frac{1}{(y - 8)^2}$**

12. $\frac{w^{18n}}{w^{22n}}$ **$\frac{1}{w^{4n}}$**
13. $\frac{z^{12k} \cdot z^{3k}}{z^{8k}}$ **z^{7k}**

14. $\frac{t^7}{t^{-2} \cdot t^0}$ **t^9**
15. $\frac{v^{-5}}{v^{-10}}$ **v^5**

16. $\frac{4x^6 + 3x^6}{x^6}$ **7**
17. $\frac{9y^3 - 3y^3}{3y^3}$ **2**

■**PROPERTIES** *Objective E*
In 18 and 19, tell whether the statement is true or false.

18. $\frac{a^{16}}{a^8} = a^2$ **false**
19. $\frac{c^{9n}}{c^{3n}} = c^{6n}$ **true**

■**USES** *Objective H*
20. In 1981, there were about $1.6 \cdot 10^8$ registered vehicles (autos, buses, trucks) in the U.S. If there were $1.12 \cdot 10^{11}$ gallons of fuel consumed, how many gallons per vehicle was this? **700 gallons**

21. In 1986, $1.93 \cdot 10^{10}$ pounds of beef were consumed in the U.S. If at the end of 1986 the U.S. population was 242.2 million people, how many pounds per person was this? **79.7 lb**

LESSON MASTER 9-8
QUESTIONS ON **SPUR** OBJECTIVES

■**SKILLS** *Objective A* (See pages 471–473 for objectives.)
In 1–4, evaluate.

1. 2^3 __8__ **2.** 3^2 __9__ **3.** $(-2)^4$ __16__ **4.** -2^4 __-16__

■**SKILLS** *Objective C*
In 5–24, simplify.

5. $(2a)^3$ __$8a^3$__ **6.** $(3x^3)^2$ __$9x^6$__

7. $5(4y)^2$ __$80y^2$__ **8.** $7(b^5)^3$ __$7b^{15}$__

9. $\left(\frac{t}{2}\right)^4$ __$\frac{t^4}{16}$__ **10.** $\left(\frac{2w^2}{3}\right)^5$ __$\frac{32w^{10}}{243}$__

11. $\left(\frac{k^5}{3}\right)^4$ __$\frac{k^{20}}{81}$__ **12.** $\left(\frac{2b^4c^7}{5}\right)^2$ __$\frac{4b^8c^{14}}{25}$__

13. $(2.5y^2)^3$ __$15.625y^6$__ **14.** $0.61(3c^5)^4$ __$49.41c^{20}$__

15. $(r^m)^n$ __r^{mn}__ **16.** $(2x^q)^0$ __1__

17. $\left(\frac{a}{b}\right)^n$ __$\frac{a^n}{b^n}$__ **18.** $\left(\frac{x^n}{y^2}\right)^3$ __$\frac{x^{3n}}{y^6}$__

■**PROPERTIES** *Objective E*
In 19 and 20, name the property which justifies the statement.

19. $\left(\frac{x}{y}\right)^5 = \frac{x^5}{y^5}$ **Power of a Quotient**

20. $(a^m b^n)^3 = a^{3m} b^{3n}$ **Power of a Product**

■**USES** *Objective H*

21. A square section of land is one mile on a side. (Recall that there are $5.28 \cdot 10^3$ feet in a mile.) What is the area of the section in square feet?

2.79×10^7 sq ft

22. The planet Mercury, shaped nearly like a sphere, has a diameter of about 3031 miles. What is the volume of Mercury in cubic miles? (Recall that the volume of a sphere is $\frac{4}{3}\pi r^3$.)

about 1.46×10^{10} cubic miles

LESSON MASTER 9-9
QUESTIONS ON **SPUR** OBJECTIVES

■**SKILLS** *Objective A* (See pages 471–473 for objectives.)
In 1–4, choose the best answer, then check it by testing a special case.

1. $n^2 n^3 =$ b; sample: $3^2 \cdot 3^3 = 9 \cdot 27 = 243 = 3^5$

(a) n^6 (b) n^5 (c) n^9 (d) n^1

2. $(n^2)^3 =$ a; sample: $(3^2)^3 = (9)^3 = 729 = 3^6$

(a) n^6 (b) n^5 (c) n^9 (d) n^1

3. $\frac{x^6}{x^2} =$ d; sample: $\frac{3^6}{3^2} = \frac{729}{9} = 81 = 3^4$

(a) x^8 (b) x^{12} (c) x^3 (d) x^4

4. $\left(\frac{x^a}{x^b}\right)^{-1} =$ a; sample: $\left(\frac{3^2}{3^3}\right)^{-1} = \left(\frac{9}{81}\right)^{-1} = \frac{81}{9} = 9 = 3^2 = 3^{4-2}$

(a) x^{b-a} (b) x^{a-b} (c) $x^{\frac{a}{b}}$ (d) $x^{\frac{b}{a}}$

■**PROPERTIES** *Objective D*
In 5–8, a. find a value of the variable for which the pattern is true; b. find a value for which the pattern is false.

5. $x^2 + x^2 = x^4$
a. __0 or $\sqrt{2}$ or $-\sqrt{2}$__
b. __any $x \neq 0$, $\sqrt{2}$, $-\sqrt{2}$__

6. $(x^2)^3 = x^5$
a. __1 or 0__
b. __any $x \neq 0$, 1__

7. $(a + b)^2 = a^2 + b^2$
a. __$a = 0$, $b \in R$ or $b = 0$, $a \in R$__
b. __$a \neq 0$, $b \neq 0$__

8. $2^x = x^2$
a. __$x = 2$ or 4__
b. __$x \neq 2, 4$__

9. Jason claimed that $x^2 + x + 1$ is a prime number for any nonzero whole number x.

a. Find at least 3 numbers for which he is right. __1__ , __2__ , __3__

b. Find a counterexample. __4__

LESSON MASTER 10-1
QUESTIONS ON **SPUR** OBJECTIVES

■**SKILLS** *Objective A* (See pages 527–529 for objectives.)
In 1–3, classify each polynomial as a monomial, binomial, or trinomial.
1. $4 - 3x$ **2.** $3ab$ **3.** $4n^2 - 3n + 2$

binomial   **monomial**   **trinomial**

In 4–6, give the degree of each polynomial.
4. $17 - 6y$ **5.** $3t^2 - 5t + 7t^3 - 10$ **6.** $4x^2$

__1__   __3__   __2__

In 7 and 8, write the polynomial in descending order of exponents.
7. $12 + 2x^3 - 4x^2 + x^5$ **8.** $8y - 6y^2 + 5 + 3y^3$

$x^5 + 2x^3 - 4x^2 + 12$ $3y^3 - 6y^2 + 8y + 5$

In 9 and 10, evaluate.
9. $6x^2 - 2x + 1$ when $x = -3$ **10.** $8a^3 - 4a^2 + 3a - 2$ when $a = \frac{1}{2}$

__61__   __$-\frac{1}{2}$__

■**USES** *Objective I*

11. For three consecutive years, Mr. Sandberg's annual deposits in his Individual Retirement Account (IRA) were $1000, $1500, and $2000. If the account had an annual yield of 8%, how much did he have in his account at the end of the third year?

$5169.31

12. At each annual baseball card show, Tim buys baseball cards. The first year he spent $20, the second, $30, the third, $50, and the fourth, $50. If the value of the cards in his collection increases by 10% each year, how much will the collection be worth at the end of the fourth year?

$184.71

13. If a ball is thrown upward at 57 ft/sec from a height of 3 ft, its distance s above the ground after t seconds is given by the formula $s = -16t^2 + 57t + 3$. How far above the ground will it be

a. after 2 seconds? **53 feet**

b. after 3 seconds? **30 feet**

c. Why is it lower after 3 seconds than after 2 seconds? **At some point, it stopped rising and began to fall.**

LESSON MASTER 10-2
QUESTIONS ON **SPUR** OBJECTIVES

■**SKILLS** *Objective A* (See pages 527–529 for objectives.)
In 1–8, simplify.
1. $(h - 3) + (2h + 6)$ **2.** $(3h^2 + 7h - 6) + (4h - 9)$
$3h + 3$ $3h^2 + 11h - 15$

3. $(16 - 7x^2) + (9 - 4x + 2x^2)$ **4.** $(4t - 9) - (3t + 8)$
$25 - 4x - 5x^2$ $t - 17$

5. $(9r - 7) - (3r - 4) - (r - 6)$ **6.** $(11 - 5w^2) - (18 - 8w^2)$
$5r + 3$ $3w^2 - 7$

7. $(10k^2 - 5k + 32) - (2k^2 - 3k + 6)$ $8k^2 - 2k + 26$

8. $(4y^4 + 6y^3 - 5y^2 - 11y) + (y^4 - y^3 + 12y)$ $5y^4 + 5y^3 - 5y^2 + y$

■**USES** *Objective I*
9. Jack has two accounts, each with an annual scale factor of y. In one account he deposits $150 a year, and in the other account he deposits $250 a year.
a. How much does he have in both accounts combined after four years?

$(400y^4 + 400y^3 + 400y^2 + 400y)$

b. If each account pays 7% interest, what is the total after four years?

$1900.30

10. If a rocket is shot upward from the surface of the earth at 500 ft/sec, its distance s above the ground after t seconds is given by $s = 500t - 16t^2$. If a rocket is shot upward from the surface of the moon, then $s = 500t - 2.7t^2$. For the times that the rocket is actually in flight, how many feet higher will it go on the moon than on the earth after t seconds?

$13.3t^2$ feet

■**REPRESENTATIONS** *Objective J*
In 11 and 12, write an expression for the shaded area. Each quadrilateral shown is a rectangle.
11.

$4x^2$

12.

$6x + 20y$

LESSON MASTER 10-3
QUESTIONS ON **SPUR** OBJECTIVES

■**SKILLS** *Objective B* (See pages 527–529 for objectives.)
In 1–6, multiply.

1. $6(x - 3x^2)$
$$6x - 18x^2$$

2. $4r(r^2 + 2r + 3)$
$$4r^3 + 8r^2 + 12r$$

3. $(4y - 11)(-3x)$
$$-12xy + 33x$$

4. $-5a(2a^2 - 3a - 10)$
$$-10a^3 + 15a^2 + 50a$$

5. $\frac{1}{6}a^2(2a^2 - 3b^2)$
$$\frac{1}{3}a^4 - \frac{1}{2}a^2b^2$$

6. $-6xy(2x - 8y^3)$
$$-12x^2y + 48xy^4$$

■**USES** *Objective I*

7. Gilbert received $110 on his 16th birthday, $140 on his 17th birthday, and $155 on his 18th birthday, which he invested after every birthday at a scale factor x. He kept his money invested at the same scale factor for 3 more years after his 18th birthday. How much money did he have at the end of this period?
$$\$(110x^5 + 140x^4 + 155x^3)$$

8. If Gilbert invests the amount in Question 7 at a different scale factor y, how much more will he have after three more years?
$$\$(110x^5y^3 + 140x^4y^3 + 155x^3y^3)$$

■**REPRESENTATIONS** *Objective J*
Refer to the diagram at the right.

9. a. Find the area of the shaded region.
$$21x^2 - 5x$$

  b. The shaded region is the amount of usable space on each floor of a building. If a company rents three full floors, how much space will the company have?
$$63x^2 - 15x$$

LESSON MASTER 10-4
QUESTIONS ON **SPUR** OBJECTIVES

■**SKILLS** *Objective D* (See pages 527–529 for objectives.)
In 1–5, fill in the blanks.

1. $6x^2 + 18x = 6x(\underline{x} + \underline{3})$

2. $4y^2 - 6y = 2y(\underline{2y} - \underline{3})$

3. $-8a^3 - 4a = -4a(\underline{2a^2} + \underline{1})$

4. $-9n^4 - 6n^2 = -3n^2(\underline{3n^2} + \underline{2})$

5. $12n^3 - 21n^2 + 27n = 3n(\underline{4n^2} - \underline{7n} + \underline{9})$

In 6 and 7, find the largest common factor.

6. $-24b^3x, 32b^4x, 48b^2$
$$8b^2$$

7. $14r^2s^2, 63r^3s, -42r^2s^3$
$$7r^2s$$

In 8–13, factor.

8. $2k^3 + 3k^3$
$$k^3(2k^2 + 3)$$

9. $6x^2 + 3$
$$3(2x^2 + 1)$$

10. $12c^3 - 15ac^2 - 18c$
$$3c(4c^2 - 5ac - 6)$$

11. $x^3y^2 - x^3y^3 + x^2y^2$
$$x^2y^2(x - y + 1)$$

12. $-3y^2z - 9yz - 12z$
$$-3z(y^2 + 3y + 4)$$

13. $25p^4q^3 + 20p^3q^4 - 35p^2q^3$
$$5p^2q^3(5p^2 + 4pq - 7)$$

In 14–17, simplify.

14. $\frac{3a^2 + a}{a}$
$$3a + 1$$

15. $\frac{16r^2 - 8t}{4t}$
$$4t - 2$$

16. $\frac{4d^3 - 6d^2 + 2d}{2d}$
$$2d^2 - 3d + 1$$

17. $\frac{9f^3 + 6f^2}{3f^2}$
$$3f + 2$$

LESSON MASTER 10-5
QUESTIONS ON **SPUR** OBJECTIVES

■**SKILLS** *Objective B* (See pages 527–529 for objectives.)
In 1–12, multiply and simplify.

1. $(x + 4)(x - 6)$
$$x^2 - 2x - 24$$

2. $(2a - 8)(a - 5)$
$$2a^2 - 18a + 40$$

3. $(5r + 4)(3r + 2)$
$$15r^2 + 22r + 8$$

4. $(11k - 3)(2k + 9)$
$$22k^2 + 93k - 27$$

5. $(7x + 2y)(3x + 4y)$
$$21x^2 + 34xy + 8y^2$$

6. $(x^2 + 2)(x^2 - 3)$
$$x^4 - x^2 - 6$$

7. $(2y - 1)(y^2 - 3y - 1)$
$$2y^3 - 7y^2 + y + 1$$

8. $(a + b + 1)(a - b - 1)$
$$a^2 - b^2 - 2b - 1$$

9. $(2x - y + 3)(x - y - 1)$
$$2x^2 + y^2 - 3xy + x - 2y - 3$$

10. $(t^2 - 1)(t^4 + t^2 + 1)$
$$t^6 - 1$$

11. $(P^3 - 2)(P^3 - 1)$
$$P^6 - 3P^3 + 2$$

12. $(a + 1)(a - 3)(a + 4)$
$$a^3 + 2a^2 - 11a - 12$$

■**REPRESENTATIONS** *Objective J*
In 13 and 14, write the area of the largest rectangle as a. the sum of terms and b. as the product of two polynomials.

13. a. $\underline{x^2 + xy + 4x + 3y + 3}$

  b. $\underline{(x + y + 1)(x + 3)}$

14. a. $\underline{ba + ca + 2a + b^2 + cb + 4b + 2c + 4}$

  b. $\underline{(b + c + 2)(a + b + 2)}$

LESSON MASTER 10-6
QUESTIONS ON **SPUR** OBJECTIVES

■**SKILLS** *Objective B* (See pages 527–529 for objectives.)
In 1–14, multiply and simplify.

1. $(x + 4)(x + 1)$
$$x^2 + 5x + 4$$

2. $(a - 4)(a - 3)$
$$a^2 - 7a + 12$$

3. $(2w - 3)(w + 5)$
$$2w^2 + 7w - 15$$

4. $(5t + 3)(3t - 5)$
$$15t^2 - 16t - 15$$

5. $(9a + 2b)(3a + b)$
$$27a^2 + 15ab + 2b^2$$

6. $(7x - y)(x - y)$
$$7x^2 - 8xy + y^2$$

7. $(x + y)(x + y)$
$$x^2 + 2xy + y^2$$

8. $(2y - z)(2y - z)$
$$4y^2 - 4yz + z^2$$

9. $(r + s)(r - s)$
$$r^2 - s^2$$

10. $(4d - 1)(4d + 1)$
$$16d^2 - 1$$

11. $(x^2 + 1)(x^2 - 2)$
$$x^4 - x^2 - 2$$

12. $(A^2 + 4)(A^2 + 3)$
$$A^4 + 7A^2 + 12$$

13. $2y(2y - 1)(y - 3)$
$$4y^3 - 14y^2 + 6y$$

14. $(a - 2)(a + 2)(a + 1)$
$$a^3 + a^2 - 4a - 4$$

■**USES** *Objective I*

15. Cindy can wear any of s sweaters or b blouses, with j jeans or k skirts. How many outfits are possible?
$$(s + b)(j + k)$$

16. On a restaurant menu, you may select one item from m meats and f fish. You may also select one item from a second list of v vegetables and p potatoes. How many different meals can you order?
$$(m + f)(v + p)$$

LESSON MASTER 10–7
QUESTIONS ON **SPUR** OBJECTIVES

■**SKILLS** *Objective B* (See pages 527–529 for objectives.)
In 1–8, expand and simplify.

1. $(t + 3)^2$

$$t^2 + 6t + 9$$

2. $(r - 5)^2$

$$r^2 - 10r + 25$$

3. $(3x + 4)^2$

$$9x^2 + 24x + 16$$

4. $(10x - y)^2$

$$100x^2 - 20xy + y^2$$

5. $(7 - 2a)^2$

$$49 - 28a + 4a^2$$

6. $3(2k - 1)^2$

$$12k^2 - 12k + 3$$

7. $2x(x + 3)^2$

$$2x^3 + 12x^2 + 18x$$

8. $y^2 - (y - 6)^2$

$$12y - 36$$

9. Show that $(a - 5)^2$ and $(5 - a)^2$ are equal.

$(a - 5)^2$	$(5 - a)^2$
$= (a - 5)(a - 5)$	$= (5 - a)(5 - a)$
$= a^2 - 10a + 25$	$= 25 - 10a + a^2$
	$= a^2 - 10a + 25$

■**PROPERTIES** *Objective F*
In 10–15, show how to calculate in your head by using the square of a binomial.

10. 51^2 $(50 + 1)^2 = 2601$

11. 19^2 $(20 - 1)^2 = 361$

12. $(1.02)^2$ $(1 + .02)^2 = 1.0404$

13. $(0.98)^2$ $(1 - .02)^2 = .9604$

14. 201^2 $(200 + 1)^2 = 40,401$

15. 103^2 $(100 + 3)^2 = 10,609$

LESSON MASTER 10–8
QUESTIONS ON **SPUR** OBJECTIVES

■**SKILLS** *Objective C* (See pages 527–529 for objectives.)
In 1–4, determine if the number is a perfect square.

1. 262 no   **2.** 289 yes   **3.** 123 no   **4.** 200 no

In 5–10, state whether the trinomial is a perfect square trinomial.

5. $x^2 + 4x + 4$ yes

6. $2y^2 - 6y + 9$ no

7. $36a^2 - 30a + 25$ no

8. $49t^2 + 42t - 9$ no

9. $4n^2 - 36nk + 81k^2$ yes

10. $144x^2 + 24xy + y^2$ yes

■**SKILLS** *Objective E*
In 11–18, write each perfect square trinomial as the square of a binomial. Otherwise, write "not a perfect square."

11. $w^2 + 18w + 81$ $(w + 9)^2$

12. $9a^2 - 12a + 4$ $(3a - 2)^2$

13. $100h^2 + 30h + 9$ not a per. sq.

14. $x^2 + 22xy + 121y^2$ $(x + 11y)^2$

15. $25a^2 - 80ab + 64b^2$ $(5a - 8b)^2$

16. $16u^2 + 56uv + 49v^2$ $(4u + 7v)^2$

17. $x^4 + 2x^2 + 1$ $(x^2 + 1)^2$

18. $d^2 + 4cd - 4c^2$ not a per. sq.

In 19–22, solve.

19. $(x - 2)^2 = 9$ $x = 5$ or -1

20. $(n + 7)^2 = 361$ $n = 12$ or -26

21. $(3t - 5)^2 = 225$ $t = \dfrac{20}{3}$ or $-\dfrac{10}{3}$

22. $3025 = (9 - d)^2$ $d = 64$ or -46

LESSON MASTER 10–9
QUESTIONS ON **SPUR** OBJECTIVES

■**SKILLS** *Objective B* (See pages 527–529 for objectives.)
In 1–8, multiply and simplify.

1. $(x + 5)(x - 5)$ $x^2 - 25$

2. $(2y - 3)(2y + 3)$ $4y^2 - 9$

3. $(9a + 4b)(9a - 4b)$ $81a^2 - 16b$

4. $(2pr - 7)(2pr + 7)$ $4p^2r^2 - 49$

5. $(y - \sqrt{10})(y + \sqrt{10})$ $y^2 - 10$

6. $\left(a - \dfrac{1}{b}\right)\left(a + \dfrac{1}{b}\right)$ $a^2 - \dfrac{1}{b^2}$

7. $x(3x + 2)(3x - 2)$ $9x^3 - 4x$

8. $2y(y - 6)(y + 6)$ $2y^3 - 72y$

■**SKILLS** *Objective E*
In 9–14, write each difference of squares as the product of two binomials. Otherwise, write "not a difference of squares."

9. $t^2 - 24$ not a diff. of sq.

10. $9w^2 - 64$ $(3w + 8)(3w - 8)$

11. $144b^2 - 25c^2$ $(12b + 5c)(12b - 5c)$

12. $z^2 - 0.01$ $(z + 0.1)(z - 0.1)$

13. $0.16x^2 - 81$ $(0.4x + 9)(0.4x - 9)$

14. $\dfrac{4}{9}p^2 - 49q^2$ $\left(\dfrac{2}{3}p + 7q\right)\left(\dfrac{2}{3}p - 7q\right)$

■**PROPERTIES** *Objective F*
In 15–18, show how to calculate mentally by multiplying binomials.

15. $19 \cdot 21$ $(20 - 1)(20 + 1) = 399$

16. $7.8 \cdot 8.2$ $(8 - 0.2)(8 + 0.2) = 63.96$

17. $100.1 \cdot 99.9$ $(100 + 0.1)(100 - 0.1) = 9999.99$

18. $6\frac{1}{2} \cdot 7\frac{1}{2}$ $\left(7 - \dfrac{1}{2}\right)\left(7 + \dfrac{1}{2}\right) = 48\frac{3}{4}$

LESSON MASTER 10–10
QUESTIONS ON **SPUR** OBJECTIVES

■**PROPERTIES** *Objective G* (See pages 527–529 for objectives.)
1. In which of the following can the Zero Product Property be used to solve the equation?

(a) $(x + 5)(x - 1) = 4$ (b) $(3y + 4)(2y - 5) = 9$
(c) $c^2 - 4c = 0$ (d) $t(t - 8)(4t + 6) = 0$ c, d

In 2–13, solve.

2. $x(x - 8) = 0$ $x = 0$ or 8

3. $-3y(2y - 8) = 0$ $y = 0$ or 4

4. $(L - 7)(4L + 9) = 0$ $L = 7$ or $-\dfrac{9}{4}$

5. $(2W + 12)(3W + 21) = 0$ $W = -6$ or -7

6. $0 = (a - 0.4)(a + 0.9)$ $a = 0.4$ or -0.9

7. $(3b - 2.1)(2b + 4.6) = 0$ $b = 0.7$ or -2.3

8. $0 = x(3x + 18)(2x - 9)$ $x = 0, -6,$ or $\dfrac{9}{2}$

9. $0 = -3a(a + 15)(2a - 7)$ $a = 0, -15,$ or $\dfrac{7}{2}$

10. $(z - 4)(z + 14)(z + 23) = 0$ $z = 4, -14,$ or -23

11. $0 = (3k + 7)(5k - 8)(4k - 13)$ $k = -\dfrac{7}{3}, \dfrac{8}{5},$ or $\dfrac{13}{4}$

12. $4x^2 - 8x = 0$ $x = 0$ or 2

13. $5v^2 = 35v$ $v = 0$ or 7

■**USES** *Objective I*
14. An arrow is shot into the air at 120 feet per second. The distance d above the ground after t seconds is $d = 120t - 16t^2$. After how many seconds will the arrow hit the ground?

7.5 seconds

15. An arrow is shot up on Mars at 120 feet per second. The distance d above the ground after t seconds is $d = 120t - 6t^2$. After how many seconds will the arrow hit the surface of Mars?

20 seconds

LESSON MASTER 10–11
QUESTIONS ON **SPUR** OBJECTIVES

■**PROPERTIES** *Objective H (See pages 527–529 for objectives.)*
In 1 and 2, answer the question by a. multiplying the binomials, b. testing two special cases.

1. Is $x^2 - 4x + 3$ equal to $(x - 3)(x - 1)$?

a. __yes__ b. __sample: $x = 1$; $1 - 4 + 3 = (-2)(0)$__

__sample: $x = 0$; $3 = (-3)(-1)$__

2. Is $2a^2 - 3a - 20$ equal to $(2a + 5)(a - 4)$?

a. __yes__ b. __sample: $a = 1$; $2 - 3 - 20 = (7)(-3)$__

__sample: $a = 0$; $-20 = (5)(-4)$__

In 3–8, choose the best answer or write none.

3. $t^2 - 5t - 14 =$ ___?___ __b__
(a) $(t + 7)(t - 2)$ (b) $(t - 7)(t + 2)$
(c) $(t + 7)(t + 2)$ (d) $(t - 7)(t - 2)$

4. $4b^2 + 27b + 18 =$ ___?___ __c__
(a) $(2b + 9)(2b + 2)$ (b) $(2b + 6)(2b + 3)$
(c) $(4b + 3)(b + 6)$ (d) $(4b + 6)(b + 3)$

5. $6x^2 + 5x - 6 =$ ___?___ __none__
(a) $(3x + 2)(2x + 3)$ (b) $(3x - 2)(2x - 3)$
(c) $(3x + 2)(2x - 3)$ (d) $(6x + 1)(x - 6)$

6. $x^2 - 2xy + 3x - 6y =$ ___?___ __a__
(a) $(x + 3)(x - 2y)$ (b) $(x - 3)(x + 2y)$
(c) $(x + 3y)(x - 2)$ (d) $(x - 3y)(x + 2)$

7. $ac - bc + ad - bd =$ ___?___ __d__
(a) $(a + b)(c - d)$ (b) $(a + d)(b - c)$
(c) $(a - d)(b + c)$ (d) $(a - b)(c + d)$

8. $x^3 - x^2 - 6x =$ ___?___ __c__
(a) $(x^2 - 3)(x + 2)$ (b) $(x^2 + 2)(x - 3)$
(c) $x(x - 3)(x + 2)$ (d) $x(x + 3)(x - 2)$

LESSON MASTER 11–1
QUESTIONS ON **SPUR** OBJECTIVES

■**REPRESENTATIONS** *Objective H (See pages 583–585 for objectives.)*
In 1–8, solve each system by graphing.

1. $\begin{cases} y = x - 6 \\ y = -2x \end{cases}$ __(2, -4)__ **2.** $\begin{cases} y = 3x - 9 \\ 6x - 2y = 10 \end{cases}$ __no sol.__

3. $\begin{cases} x + y = 5 \\ x - y = 3 \end{cases}$ __(4, 1)__ **4.** $\begin{cases} 2x + y = 4 \\ 3y = 2x - 12 \end{cases}$ __(3, -2)__

5. $\begin{cases} 2x - 5y = 3 \\ 4y - x = -3 \end{cases}$ __(-1, -1)__ **6.** $\begin{cases} \frac{y}{2} = x + 3 \\ y = 2x + 6 \end{cases}$ __inf. many__

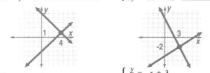

7. $\begin{cases} 12 = 3x + 2y \\ -10 = x + 2y \end{cases}$ __$(11, -\frac{21}{2})$__ **8.** $\begin{cases} 7y = 4 - x \\ x = -12 - 7y \end{cases}$ __no sol.__

LESSON MASTER 11–2
QUESTIONS ON **SPUR** OBJECTIVES

■**SKILLS** *Objective A (See pages 583–585 for objectives.)*
In 1–8, solve each system of equations.

1. $\begin{cases} y = 2x - 7 \\ y = 5 - x \end{cases}$ __$x = 4$, $y = 1$__

2. $\begin{cases} b = 2a - 1 \\ 2a - 3b = 7 \end{cases}$ __$a = -1$, $b = -3$__

3. $\begin{cases} r = 2t \\ 3r - 5t = 2 \end{cases}$ __$r = 4$, $t = 2$__

4. $\begin{cases} m = 3n - 5 \\ n + 4m = 6 \end{cases}$ __$m = 1$, $n = 2$__

5. $\begin{cases} x = 3n \\ y = 4n \\ 2x + y = 120 \end{cases}$ __$n = 12$, $x = 36$, $y = 48$__

6. $\begin{cases} x = 5p \\ y = -2p \\ x - 4y = 52 \end{cases}$ __$p = 4$, $x = 20$, $y = -8$__

7. $\begin{cases} h = 4k \\ 3h + 2k = 21 \end{cases}$ __$h = 6$, $k = \frac{3}{2}$__

8. $\begin{cases} x = 2 - y \\ x = 5 + 3y \end{cases}$ __$x = \frac{11}{4}$, $y = -\frac{3}{4}$__

■**USES** *Objective F*
9. A boat can travel r mph in still water. This is three times as fast as the current, c, in a river. The boat can go downstream at 12 mph. What is the speed of the boat and the speed of the current?

__$r = 9$ mph, $c = 3$ mph__

10. Helen earned $240 in the summer by working at a fast food restaurant and baby-sitting. If she earned five times as much in the restaurant as she did baby-sitting, how much did she earn at each job?

__$200 at the restaurant, $40 baby-sitting__

11. In 14-carat gold, there are 14 units of gold for every 10 units of other metal. If a 14-carat gold pendant weighs 0.72 ounces, how much pure gold is in it?

__0.42 ounces__

LESSON MASTER 11–3
QUESTIONS ON **SPUR** OBJECTIVES

■**SKILLS** *Objective A (See pages 583–585 for objectives.)*
In 1–8, find the point of intersection of the lines with the given equations.

1. $\begin{cases} y = 3x + 1 \\ y = x - 9 \end{cases}$ __$x = -5$, $y = -14$__

2. $\begin{cases} r = 11 - s \\ r = -3s + 9 \end{cases}$ __$r = 12$, $s = -1$__

3. $\begin{cases} p = 0.4q + 1.6 \\ p = 0.2q - 1.8 \end{cases}$ __$p = -5.2$, $q = -17$__

4. $\begin{cases} u = 0.6v - 3.2 \\ u = 0.3v - 3.1 \end{cases}$ __$u = -3$, $v = \frac{1}{3}$__

5. $\begin{cases} y = \frac{1}{2}x - \frac{1}{3} \\ y = \frac{1}{6}x + \frac{1}{4} \end{cases}$ __$x = \frac{7}{4}$, $y = \frac{13}{24}$__

6. $\begin{cases} a = \frac{2}{3}b + \frac{1}{2} \\ a = \frac{1}{6}b + \frac{1}{3} \end{cases}$ __$a = \frac{5}{18}$, $b = -\frac{1}{3}$__

■**USES** *Objective F*
7. A tortoise and a hare are racing. The tortoise goes one foot per second and the hare runs 13 feet per second. The tortoise has a 24 ft head start. (The hare must travel 24 ft more than the tortoise.) How many feet will the hare have to run to catch up with the tortoise?

__26 feet__

8. For a certain call one long distance phone company charges $2 for the first three minutes and 60 cents for each additional minute. Another company charges $1.50 for the first three minutes and 70 cents for each additional minute for the same call. After how many minutes beyond three minutes will the total charge be the same for both companies?

__5 minutes__

LESSON MASTER 11–4
QUESTIONS ON **SPUR** OBJECTIVES

■ **SKILLS** *Objective B (See pages 583–585 for objectives.)*
In 1–10, solve each system of equations.

1. $\begin{cases} 2x - y = 7 \\ x + y = 5 \end{cases}$ **$x = 4, y = 1$**

2. $\begin{cases} 3h - k = 7 \\ 2h + k = 8 \end{cases}$ **$h = 3, k = 2$**

3. $\begin{cases} 3u + 2v = 18 \\ 5u - 2v = 14 \end{cases}$ **$u = 4, v = 3$**

4. $\begin{cases} 2a + b = 9 \\ 2a - 3b = 5 \end{cases}$ **$a = 4, b = 1$**

5. $\begin{cases} 2r - 3s = 1 \\ 2r - 4s = 2 \end{cases}$ **$r = -1, s = -1$**

6. $\begin{cases} 4x - 3y = 30 \\ 7x - 3y = 48 \end{cases}$ **$x = 6, y = -2$**

7. $\begin{cases} \frac{5}{6}c - d = 2 \\ \frac{2}{3}c + d = 16 \end{cases}$ **$c = 12, d = 8$**

8. $\begin{cases} \frac{3}{4}a + \frac{1}{6}b = 6 \\ \frac{1}{2}a - \frac{1}{3}b = 4 \end{cases}$ **$a = 8, b = 0$**

9. $\begin{cases} .04x + .02y = 1.8 \\ .04x - .01y = 1.5 \end{cases}$ **$x = 40, y = 10$**

10. $\begin{cases} .7y + .2z = 11 \\ .4y - .2z = 11 \end{cases}$ **$y = 20, z = -15$**

■ **USES** *Objective F*

11. The sum of two numbers is 79 and their difference is 5. What are the numbers?

37 and 42

12. Three hamburgers and two orders of fries cost $6.10. Four hamburgers and two orders of fries cost $7.60. At these rates, what is the cost h of one hamburger and the cost f of one order of fries?

$h = \$1.50, f = \$.80$

13. Marianne has two investments. The first pays 4% interest and the second pays 5%. The total annual interest is $130. If the first investment paid 6%, her annual interest would be $170. How much does she have invested at each rate?

at 4%: $2000; at 5%: $1000

LESSON MASTER 11–5
QUESTIONS ON **SPUR** OBJECTIVES

■ **SKILLS** *Objective C (See pages 583–585 for objectives.)*
In 1–8, solve each system of equations.

1. $\begin{cases} 5x - 2y = 3 \\ 15x + 8y = 2 \end{cases}$ **$x = \frac{2}{5}, y = -\frac{1}{2}$**

2. $\begin{cases} 2a + 3b = 2 \\ 6a - 6b = 1 \end{cases}$ **$a = \frac{1}{2}, b = \frac{1}{3}$**

3. $\begin{cases} .4x - .2y = 2 \\ .7x + .3y = 23 \end{cases}$ **$x = 20, y = 30$**

4. $\begin{cases} .05c - .3d = -2.4 \\ .4c + .17d = 6.5 \end{cases}$ **$c = 12, d = 10$**

5. $\begin{cases} \frac{1}{2}m - \frac{1}{3}n = 8 \\ \frac{3}{4}m + \frac{5}{6}n = 4 \end{cases}$ **$m = 12, n = -6$**

6. $\begin{cases} \frac{3}{4}c + \frac{2}{3}d = 8 \\ 5c + 2d = 68 \end{cases}$ **$c = 16, d = -6$**

7. $\begin{cases} 2 = 4h + 7k \\ 1 = 3h + 5k \end{cases}$ **$h = -3, k = 2$**

8. $\begin{cases} 7r = -6s + 15 \\ -3r + 10s = -1 \end{cases}$ **$r = \frac{39}{22}, s = \frac{19}{44}$**

■ **USES** *Objective F*

9. The perimeter of a rectangle is 16 cm. If the length is doubled, the perimeter is 26. What are the length and width?

length = 5 cm, width = 3 cm

10. A shipping clerk finds that 3 large cartons and 2 small cartons will hold 108 lb. He also finds that 2 large cartons and 3 small cartons hold 102 lb. How much do a large carton and a small carton hold, respectively?

large = 24 lb, small = 18 lb

11. For a school play, the eighth graders sold 220 adult tickets and 100 children's tickets. They took in $410 altogether. The ninth graders collected $366 from the sale of 180 adult tickets and 120 children's tickets. What was the price of an adult ticket and a child's ticket?

adult = $1.50, child = $.80

LESSON MASTER 11–6
QUESTIONS ON **SPUR** OBJECTIVES

■ **USES** *Objective G (See pages 583–585 for objectives.)*

1. Two large towns are 60 miles apart. For 20 miles the speed limit is 55 mph. For the rest of the distance the speed limit is 65 mph. If I travel at the speed limit for the entire trip, what will be my average speed?

$61\frac{2}{3}$ mph

2. Mark earned the following grades in high school: 6 A's, 7 B's, 4 C's, and 1 D. What is his grade point average? (Assume A = 4, B = 3, C = 2, D = 1.)

3.0

3. A final exam consists of two parts: multiple choice questions worth 100 points, and essay questions worth 150 points. Sally got 75 points on the multiple choice section and 95 points on the essay section. What is her average for the whole test?

87 points

4. "Slugger" Miller had a batting average of .220 in 120 times at bat on natural grass, and an average of .310 in 180 times at bat on artificial turf. What was his overall batting average?

.274

5. Pure gold is 24 carat. A jeweler mixes 1.2 oz of 14-carat gold with 1.8 oz of 18-carat gold. What is the carat value (purity) of the mixture?

16.4 carat

6. A meat manufacturer makes up packages of lunchmeat containing 10 slices of ham worth $.15 each, 8 slices of chicken worth $.12 each and 6 slices of bologna worth $.10 each. How much should he sell the mixture for so as not to lose money?

$3.06

7. A boat travels 12 miles downstream at 4 mph, and returns upstream the same distance at 3 mph. What is the average speed for the whole trip?

$3\frac{3}{7}$ mph

LESSON MASTER 11–7
QUESTIONS ON **SPUR** OBJECTIVES

■ **USES** *Objective G (See pages 583–585 for objectives.)*

1. At the Math Club bake sale, 20 slices of date-nut bread were sold for 25 cents a slice. There were 10 slices left over. How much should members pay for a leftover slice so that the overall average price per slice is 21 cents?

13 cents

2. After 8 tests Mario has an average of 78. The final exam is worth 2 tests. The minimum average for a B is 80. What minimum grade does he have to make on the final in order to make a B?

88

3. Because of heavy traffic a bus averages 20 mph for the first 2 hours of a trip. How long must the bus travel at 60 mph in order to average 40 mph for the entire trip up to that point?

2 hours

4. In 15 basketball games, Ken has been averaging 18 points a game. How many more games must he play at 25 points per game in order to have an overall average of 20 points per game?

6 games

5. How many liters of 60% acid solution must be added to 8 liters of a 40% acid solution to make a mixture that is 50% acid?

8 liters

6. Harry has $1200 invested at 5%. How much more money must he invest at 8% to have an overall investment of 6%?

$600

7. In a large city, there has been an average of 16 auto accidents a day for 110 days. How many consecutive accident free days must there now be in order to bring the average down to 10 per day?

66 days

LESSON MASTER 11-8
QUESTIONS ON **SPUR** OBJECTIVES

■**PROPERTIES** *Objective E* (See pages 583–585 for objectives.)
In 1–8, a. determine the number of solutions to each system. b. Are the lines parallel?

1. $\begin{cases} 3x - 5y = 9 \\ 12x - 20y = 36 \end{cases}$
a. **inf. many** b. **yes**

2. $\begin{cases} 2x + 8y = -20 \\ x - 4y = -10 \end{cases}$
a. **one** b. **no**

3. $\begin{cases} 2a = b + 11 \\ 2a = b - 11 \end{cases}$
a. **no sol.** b. **yes**

4. $\begin{cases} 8p = 12 - 2q \\ q + 4p = 6 \end{cases}$
a. **inf. many** b. **yes**

5. $\begin{cases} 2(m + 4) = 3(n - 2) \\ 6(m + 1) = 9(n - 4) \end{cases}$
a. **inf. many** b. **yes**

6. $\begin{cases} \frac{x}{2} + \frac{y}{5} = 1 \\ \frac{x}{4} + \frac{y}{10} = 1 \end{cases}$
a. **no sol.** b. **yes**

7. $\begin{cases} 4r = 2(t - 6) \\ 6r = 3(t - 9) \end{cases}$
a. **no sol.** b. **yes**

8. $\begin{cases} 2(x - 3) + 3(y - 1) = 6 \\ 3(x - 1) + 2(y - 3) = 6 \end{cases}$
a. **one** b. **no**

■**USES** *Objective F*
In 9 and 10, could the given situation ever happen?
9. You bought 2 pencils and 1 eraser for 20¢. At the same prices, your friend bought 4 pencils and 2 erasers for 40¢. **yes**

10. The mass of 2 pencils and 1 eraser is 40 grams. The mass of 4 pencils and 2 erasers of the same kind is 60 grams. **no**

■**REPRESENTATIONS** *Objective H*
11. *Multiple choice* Two straight lines with the same slope and same y-intercept intersect in
(a) exactly one point   (b) exactly two points
(c) no points   (d) infinitely many points   **d**

In 12 and 13, tell whether the statement is true or false.
12. Coincident lines are parallel lines. **true**
13. In a plane, two lines with different slopes must intersect. **true**

Algebra © Scott, Foresman and Company   **101**

LESSON MASTER 11-9
QUESTIONS ON **SPUR** OBJECTIVES

■**PROPERTIES** *Objective D* (See pages 583–585 for objectives.)
In 1–8, solve.

1. $3t + 1 < 3t + 4$ **t is any real number**
2. $6(x - 3) = 2(3x + 2)$ **no solution**
3. $8x + 7 > 4(2x + 2)$ **no solution**
4. $-4b + 8b < 4(b + 3)$ **b is any real number**
5. $5q - 2 = 3q - 2$ **q = 0**
6. $12w + 10 = 5(3w + 2)$ **w = 0**
7. $2(r - 3) > r - 6$ **r > 0**
8. $d + 7 = d - 7$ **no solution**

■**USES** *Objective F*
9. Sara deposited $500 in Bank A paying 5% interest. At the same time, she also deposited $500 in Bank B paying 5.5% interest. She withdrew only the interest each year and made no more deposits.
a. What sentence could you solve to find out when the account in Bank A would have earned more money?
$500(.05)t > 500(.055)t$
b. Solve the sentence to answer the question. **no sol.; The account in Bank A will never earn more money.**

10. Car rental Company X charges $29.95 a day plus $.15 per mile. Car rental Company Y charges $29.95 a day plus $.20 a mile.
a. What sentence could you solve to find out after how many miles the charges would be the same?
$29.95 + .15m = 29.95 + .20m$
b. Solve the sentence to answer the questions. **m = 0; They are the same now.**

102   Algebra © Scott, Foresman and Company

LESSON MASTER 11-10
QUESTIONS ON **SPUR** OBJECTIVES

■**REPRESENTATIONS** *Objective I* (See pages 583–585 for objectives.)
In 1–6, graph the solution set to each system.

1. $\begin{cases} x + y < 4 \\ x - y > 4 \end{cases}$

2. $\begin{cases} y < x + 3 \\ 2x + y < 3 \end{cases}$

3. $\begin{cases} x > 0 \\ y > 0 \\ x + y < 5 \end{cases}$

4. $\begin{cases} x < 0 \\ y < 0 \\ x + y > -2 \end{cases}$
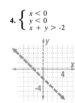

5. $\begin{cases} x > 0 \\ y > 0 \\ x < 3 \\ y < 3 \end{cases}$
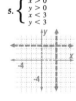

6. $\begin{cases} x \geq 0 \\ y \geq 0 \\ 2x + y > 1 \\ 2x + y < 4 \end{cases}$

In 7 and 8, write a sentence for and accurately graph the set of points which satisfy each situation.

7. The Drama Club sold tickets for a performance. They sold s student tickets and a adult tickets. The auditorium holds 80 people. How many adults and students might have bought tickets?
$a + s \leq 80$

8. The Pep Club has a total of 30 caps and buttons left. They must sell at least 10 caps or buttons to make a profit. If they made a profit, how many caps c and buttons b might they have sold?
$30 \geq (b + c) \geq 10$
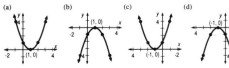

Algebra © Scott, Foresman and Company   **103**

LESSON MASTER 12-1
QUESTIONS ON **SPUR** OBJECTIVES

■**PROPERTIES** *Objective D* (See pages 633–635 for objectives.)
1. What is the shape of the graph of $y = -x^2 + 6x + 8$? **parabola**

In 2–4, tell whether the graph of the equation opens up or down.
2. $y = 3x^2$ **up**   3. $y = 9 - x^2$ **down**
4. $y = 4 - 2x + x^2$ **up**

■**REPRESENTATIONS** *Objective H*
In 5–8, a. make a table of values and b. graph the equation.

5. $y = 2x^2$
a.
x	y
0	0
1	2
-1	2
2	8
-2	8
b.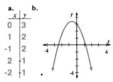

6. $y = -\frac{1}{4}x^2$
a.
x	y
0	0
2	-1
-2	-1
4	-4
-4	-4
b.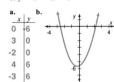

7. $y = -x^2 + 3$
a.
x	y
0	3
1	2
-1	2
2	-1
-2	-1
b.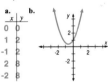

8. $y = x^2 - x - 6$
a.
x	y
0	-6
3	0
-2	0
4	6
-3	6
b.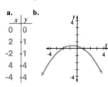

9. *Multiple choice* Which could be the graph of $y = x^2 + 2x + 1$? **c**
(a)   (b)   (c)   (d)

104   Algebra © Scott, Foresman and Company

LESSON MASTER 12–2
QUESTIONS ON **SPUR** OBJECTIVES

■**REPRESENTATIONS**   *Objective H* (See pages 633–635 for objectives.)
In 1–4, put the equation in a form in which it can be graphed with an automatic grapher.

1. $2x + y = 6$ _____ $y = -2x + 6$

2. $6x + 2y = x^2$ _____ $y = \frac{1}{2}x^2 - 3x$

3. $x^2 + y - 3x = 0$ _____ $y = -x^2 + 3x$

4. $3x^2 - 6x - 2y = 0$ _____ $y = \frac{3}{2}x^2 - 3x$

In 5–8, give a suitable window that will give a graph that includes the vertex.

vertex: sample window:

5. $y = 2x^2 + x - 1$ $(-\frac{1}{4}, -1\frac{1}{8})$; $-2 \le x \le 2$, $-2 \le y \le 10$

6. $y = x^2 - 6x + 8$ $(3, -1)$; $1 \le x \le 5$, $-2 \le y \le 4$

7. $y = x^2 - 3x + 16$ $(1\frac{1}{2}, 13\frac{3}{4})$; $0 \le x \le 3$, $12 \le y \le 18$

8. $y = 9x - x^2$ $(4\frac{1}{2}, 20\frac{1}{4})$; $3 \le x \le 7$, $17 \le y \le 21$

In 9 and 10, graph the equation and estimate the vertex.

9. $y = 3x^2 + 6x - 1$ ___ $(-1, -4)$ **10.** $y = 2x^2 - 8x + 3$ $(2, -5)$

In 11 and 12, describe the window.

11. $-14 \le x \le 12$, $-3 \le y \le 8$ **12.** $-40 \le x \le 90$, $-20 \le y \le 35$

Algebra © Scott, Foresman and Company   **105**

LESSON MASTER 12–3
QUESTIONS ON **SPUR** OBJECTIVES

■**USES**   *Objective G* (See pages 633–635 for objectives.)
1. A baseball crosses home plate at a height of 4 ft. The batter hits the ball into the air. The path of the ball is described by the equation below where h is the height of the ball in feet and x is the number of feet the ball is downfield.

$$h = -\tfrac{1}{729}(x - 162)^2 + 40.$$

The outfield wall is 6 ft high and 318 ft from home plate. Will the ball go over the wall for a home run? If so, by how many feet will it clear the wall?

yes   ≈.6 ft

2. Suppose the outfield wall in Question 1 was 324 feet from home plate. Would it be possible for an outfielder to catch the ball? If so, at what height above the ground would the ball be when he caught it with his back against the wall?

yes   4 ft

3. A ball is thrown upward from the surface of Mars with an initial velocity of 36 feet per second. Its approximate height h above the surface after a time of t seconds is given by the equation: $h = 36t - 6t^2$.

a. What is its height after 2 seconds? _____ 48 ft

b. What is its height after 6 seconds? _____ 0 ft

c. From the answer in part **b.**, after how many seconds will it reach its highest point, and how high will it be?   3 sec   54 ft

4. Refer to the graph at the right. It shows the height of a ball at a time of t seconds after it is thrown upward with an initial velocity of 30 meters per second.

a. Estimate from the graph its height h after 1 second.
_____ 25 m

b. Estimate from the graph when it will reach a height of 30 meters. $1\frac{1}{3}$ sec and $4\frac{2}{3}$ sec

c. What is the maximum height?   45 m

106   *Algebra © Scott, Foresman and Company*

LESSON MASTER 12–4
QUESTIONS ON **SPUR** OBJECTIVES

■**SKILLS**   *Objective A* (See pages 633–635 for objectives.)
In 1–6, give the exact solutions to the equation.

1. $3x^2 - 10x + 8 = 0$ **2.** $14a^2 + 13a + 3 = 0$
$x = \frac{4}{3}$ or $x = 2$ $a = -\frac{1}{2}$ or $a = -\frac{3}{7}$

3. $t^2 - 10t = -25$ **4.** $(n + 2)(n - 4) = 7$
$t = 5$ $n = -3$ or $n = 5$

5. $4r - r^2 = -21$ **6.** $10p - p^2 = 24$
$r = -3$ or $r = 7$ $p = 4$ or $p = 6$

In 7 and 8, a. find a simpler equation that has the same solution. b. Then solve the equation.

7. $3x^2 - 27x + 54 = 0$ **8.** $16y^2 + 28y - 8 = 0$
a. $x^2 - 9x + 18 = 0$ **a.** $4y^2 + 7y - 2 = 0$
b. $x = 3$ or $x = 6$ **b.** $y = -2$ or $y = -\frac{1}{4}$

In 9 and 10, solve. Approximate solutions to the nearest tenth.

9. $x^2 + 3x - 5 = 0$ **10.** $(2c - 1)(c + 2) = 5$
$x \approx -4.2$ or $x \approx 1.2$ $c \approx -2.8$ or $c \approx 1.3$

■**PROPERTIES**   *Objective E*
In 11 and 12, tell whether the statement is true or false.
11. Some quadratic equations cannot be solved using the Quadratic Formula.   false

12. To apply the Quadratic Formula, one side of a quadratic equation must be zero.   true

■**USES**   *Objective G*
13. The height h in feet of a ball thrown upward on Mars after a time of t seconds is given by $h = 48t - 6t^2$. At what times was the ball 30 feet above the surface?
at about .7 and 7.3 seconds

14. The side of a square is n cm. If the length is increased by 5 cm and the width is decreased by 4 cm, the resulting rectangle has an area of 112 square cm. What was the length of the side of the square?
11 cm

Algebra © Scott, Foresman and Company   **107**

LESSON MASTER 12–5
QUESTIONS ON **SPUR** OBJECTIVES

■**SKILLS**   *Objective A* (See pages 633–635 for objectives.)
In 1 and 2, give the exact solutions to the equation.

1. $2x^2 + 13x - 7 = 0$ **2.** $x^2 - 7x - 3 = 0$
$\frac{1}{2}, -7$ $\frac{-7 \pm \sqrt{61}}{2}$

■**PROPERTIES**   *Objective D*
In 3–6, tell how many times the graph of the equation intersects the x-axis.

3. $y = 2x^2 - 5x - 7$ **4.** $y = 7x^2 + 6x + 2$
2   none

5. $y = 4x^2 - 4x + 1$ **6.** $y = x^2 - 9x - 22$
1   2

■**PROPERTIES**   *Objective E*
In 7–9, let D be the discriminant of the equation $ax^2 + bx + c = 0$. Match the answers.

7. $D > 0$ ___ b   (a) no real solutions

8. $D = 0$ ___ c   (b) two real solutions

9. $D < 0$ ___ a   (c) one real solution

In 10–15, a. find the value of the discriminant, and b. determine the number of real solutions to the equation.

10. $5x^2 - x + 2 = 0$ **11.** $a^2 - 6a = 8$
a. -39 **b.** none   **a.** 68   **b.** 2

12. $1 + 6n + 9n^2 = 0$ **13.** $0.6k^2 - 1.39k + 2 = 0$
a. 0   **b.** 1   **a.** ≈-2.87 **b.** none

14. $1.1p^2 + 3.2p - 1.2 = 0$ **15.** $\frac{1}{4}x^2 + \frac{1}{2}x + \frac{1}{3} = 0$
a. 15.52   **b.** 2   **a.** $-\frac{1}{12}$ **b.** none

108   *Algebra © Scott, Foresman and Company*

LESSON MASTER 12–6
QUESTIONS ON **SPUR** OBJECTIVES

■**PROPERTIES**   *Objective E*   *(See pages 633–635 for objectives.)*

1. *Multiple choice* If its discriminant is a nonzero perfect square, a quadratic equation has:

(a) one real solution   (b) two irrational solutions

(c) two rational solutions   (d) none of these   **c**

In 2–7, a. use the discriminant to determine the number of real solutions. b. Tell whether the real solutions are rational or irrational.

2. $x^2 - 8x + 3 = 0$ **3.** $16a^2 + 8a + 1 = 0$

a. _____ **2** _____   a. _____ **1** _____

b. _____ **irrational** _____   b. _____ **rational** _____

4. $13y^2 - 4 = 0$ **5.** $t(t + 2) = 4$

a. _____ **2** _____   a. _____ **2** _____

b. _____ **irrational** _____   b. _____ **irrational** _____

6. $4b(b + 2) = 5$ **7.** $9r^2 + 16 = 0$

a. _____ **2** _____   a. _____ **none** _____

b. _____ **rational** _____   b. _____ **—** _____

■**PROPERTIES**   *Objective F*
In 8–13, tell whether the number is rational or irrational.

8. $\sqrt{32}$ **irrational**   **9.** 19.031 **rational**

10. $-\frac{2}{3}$ **rational**   **11.** $\frac{3\pi}{2}$ **irrational**

12. $\sqrt{144}$ **rational**   **13.** $6.\overline{4}$ **rational**

LESSON MASTER 12–7
QUESTIONS ON **SPUR** OBJECTIVES

■**SKILLS**   *Objective B*   *(See pages 633–635 for objectives.)*
In 1–12, a. use the discriminant to determine which quadratic trinomials are factorable. b. If possible, factor.

1. $t^2 + t - 12$ **2.** $r^2 + 16r + 15$
$(t + 4)(t - 3)$ $(r + 15)(r + 1)$

3. $3x^2 - 7x + 4$ **4.** $n^2 - 7n - 18$
$(3x - 4)(x - 1)$ $(n - 9)(n + 2)$

5. $y^2 + 9y + 20$ **6.** $24a^2 + 10a - 21$
$(y + 4)(y + 5)$ $(6a + 7)(4a - 3)$

7. $12c^2 + 7c - 45$ **8.** $3x^2 - 10x + 3$
$(4c + 9)(3c - 5)$ $(3x - 1)(x - 3)$

9. $2x^2 - x - 10$ **10.** $5x^2 - 14 - 3x$
$(2x - 5)(x + 2)$ $(5x + 7)(x - 3)$

11. $6 - 25t + 4t^2$ **12.** $6y^2 - 4y - 3$
$(4t - 1)(t - 6)$ not factorable

In 13–18, a. factor the trinomial into the product of a monomial and a trinomial. b. Complete the factoring by finding the factors of the trinomial.

13. $x^3 - 3x^2 + 2x$ **14.** $y^3 + 8y^2 + 12y$
a. $x(x^2 - 3x + 2)$ a. $y(y^2 + 8y + 12)$
b. $x(x - 2)(x - 1)$ b. $y(y + 6)(y + 2)$

15. $2a^3 - 6a^2 - 8a$ **16.** $r^4 + 8r^3 + 12r^2$
a. $2a(a^2 - 3a - 4)$ a. $r^2(r^2 + 8r + 12)$
b. $2a(a - 4)(a + 1)$ b. $r^2(r + 6)(r + 2)$

17. $3t^3 - 12t^2 + 12t$ **18.** $5a^4 + 10a^3 + 5a^2$
a. $3t(t^2 - 4t + 4)$ a. $5a^2(a^2 + 2a + 1)$
b. $3t(t - 2)^2$ b. $5a^2(a + 1)^2$

LESSON MASTER 12–8
QUESTIONS ON **SPUR** OBJECTIVES

■**SKILLS**   *Objective C*   *(See pages 633–635 for objectives.)*
In 1–14, solve by factoring.

1. $x^2 + 14x + 24 = 0$ **2.** $a^2 - 4a - 21 = 0$
$x = -12$ or $x = -2$ $a = -3$ or $a = 7$

3. $2y^2 + 5y - 3 = 0$ **4.** $2r^2 - 17r + 21 = 0$
$y = -3$ or $y = \frac{1}{2}$ $r = \frac{3}{2}$ or $r = 7$

5. $c^2 - 16 = 0$ **6.** $k^2 - 64 = 0$
$c = -4$ or $c = 4$ $k = -8$ or $k = 8$

7. $4t^2 + 15t = 4$ **8.** $6x^2 = x + 35$
$t = -4$ or $t = \frac{1}{4}$ $x = -\frac{7}{3}$ or $x = \frac{5}{2}$

9. $y^3 + 9y^2 + 20y = 0$ **10.** $(n - 2)(n + 3) = 6$
$y = -5$ or $y = -4$ or $y = 0$ $n = -4$ or $n = 3$

11. $(b + 1)(b + 5) = 45$ **12.** $4d^3 + 11d^2 - 3d = 0$
$b = -10$ or $b = 4$ $d = -3$ or $d = 0$ or $d = \frac{1}{4}$

13. $p^2 - 8p = 0$ **14.** $a^3 - 9a^2 = 0$
$p = 0$ or $p = 8$ $a = 0$ or $a = 9$

■**USES**   *Objective G*
15. In a round-robin tournament, 66 games were played. The expression
$$\frac{n^2 - n}{2}$$
gives the number of games played in the tournament for *n* teams. How many teams were in the tournament?   **12 teams**

16. One formula for finding the approximate stopping distance *d* (in feet) of an automobile going *x* mph on a wet road is
$$d = \frac{10x + x^2}{10}$$
If it took 20 ft to stop a car, how fast was it going?   **10 mph**

LESSON MASTER 12–9
QUESTIONS ON **SPUR** OBJECTIVES

■**SKILLS**   *Objective B*   *(See pages 633–635 for objectives.)*
In 1–4, given that *p* and *q* are solutions to the quadratic equation, write the factors of the quadratic expression.

1. $x^2 - 11x - 42 = 0$; $p = 14$, $q = -3$ $(x - 14)(x + 3)$

2. $y^2 - 28y + 96 = 0$; $p = 4$, $q = 24$ $(y - 4)(y - 24)$

3. $2a^2 - a - 36 = 0$; $p = -4$, $q = \frac{9}{2}$ $(a + 4)(2a - 9)$

4. $3c^2 + 22c + 24 = 0$; $p = -6$, $q = -\frac{4}{3}$ $(c + 6)(3c + 4)$

In 5–8, a quadratic equation is given with one of its solutions. Use this information to factor.

5. $x^2 - 39x + 108 = 0$; 3   **6.** $t^2 - 48t + 540 = 0$; 18
$(x - 3)(x - 36)$ $(t - 18)(t - 30)$

7. $4a^2 - 11a - 45 = 0$; $-\frac{9}{4}$ **8.** $12x^2 - 43x + 36 = 0$; $\frac{4}{3}$
$(4a + 9)(a - 5)$ $(3x - 4)(4x - 9)$

In 9–11, factor the expression as much as possible.

9. $2y^3 - 3y + y^2$ $y(y - 1)(2y + 3)$

10. $15x^3 + 41x^2 + 14x$ $x(5x + 2)(3x + 7)$

11. $c^4 - 36c^3 + 320c^2$ $c^2(c - 20)(c - 16)$

LESSON MASTER 13–1
QUESTIONS ON SPUR OBJECTIVES

■PROPERTIES   *Objective C*   *(See pages 673–675 for objectives.)*
In 1–6, tell whether or not the equation determines a function.

1. $x = 2y + 5$ ____ **yes**   **2.** $y = |2x - 5|$ ____ **yes**

3. $x^2 = y - 4$ ____ **yes**   **4.** $x = |y - 3|$ ____ **no**

5. $y^2 = x$ ____ **no**   **6.** $y = 100(1.06)^x$ ____ **yes**

In 7–10, tell whether or not the set of ordered pairs is a function.

7. $\{(1, 3), (2, 4), (3, 5)\}$ ____ **yes**   **8.** $\{(2, 5), (3, 5), (4, 5)\}$ ____ **yes**

9. $\{(\pi, 5), (\pi, 4), (0, 0)\}$ ____ **no**   **10.** $\{(a, b), (b, c), (c, d)\}$ ____ **yes**

■PROPERTIES   *Objective D*
In 11–14, classify the function as (a) linear, (b) quadratic, or (c) exponential.

11. $y = x(x + 2)$ ____ **b**   **12.** $y = 2^2 - x$ ____ **a**

13. $y = 2^x$ ____ **c**   **14.** $y = x^2$ ____ **b**

■REPRESENTATIONS   *Objective H*
In 15–20, tell whether or not the set of ordered pairs graphed is a function.

15. ____ **yes**   **16.** ____ **no**   **17.** ____ **yes**

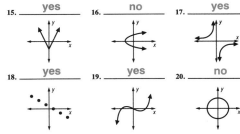

18. ____ **yes**   **19.** ____ **yes**   **20.** ____ **no**

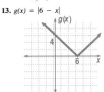

21. *True or False*   Any vertical line passing through the graph of a function will intersect the graph in no more than one point. ____ **true**

LESSON MASTER 13–2
QUESTIONS ON SPUR OBJECTIVES

■SKILLS   *Objective A*   *(See pages 673–675 for objectives.)*
In 1–6, $f(x) = x^2 - 8x + 12$. Calculate.

1. $f(2)$ ____ **0**   **2.** $f(-1)$ ____ **21**

3. $f(0)$ ____ **12**   **4.** $f(6)$ ____ **0**

5. $f(1.5)$ ____ **2.25**   **6.** $f(-\frac{9}{2})$ ____ **68.25**

7. If $s(n) = \sqrt{n - 8}$, what is $s(12)$? ____ **2**

8. If $g(x) = 2^x - 1$, find $g(2) + g(3)$. ____ **10**

9. If $A(t) = -2t + 3$, calculate $\dfrac{A(5) - A(2)}{3}$. ____ **-2**

10. If $A(r) = \pi r^2$, find $A(2)$. ____ **$4\pi \approx 12.57$**

■REPRESENTATIONS   *Objective I*
In 11–14, graph each function.

11. $f(x) = 2(x - 1)$ **12.** $g(x) = 1 - x^2$

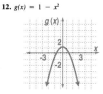

13. $h(t) = \left(\frac{1}{2}\right)^t$ **14.** $k(n) = 5$, n an integer between -2 and 2.

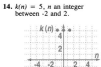

LESSON MASTER 13–3
QUESTIONS ON SPUR OBJECTIVES

■SKILLS   *Objective A*   *(See pages 673–675 for objectives.)*
In 1–6, $f(x) = |24 - x|$. Calculate.

1. $f(36)$ ____ **12**   **2.** $f(0)$ ____ **24**

3. $f(-6)$ ____ **30**   **4.** $10 - f(28)$ ____ **6**

5. $f(20.5) + f(22.5)$ ____ **5**   **6.** $f(-3.5) - f(-1.5)$ ____ **2**

In 7 and 8, $g(t) = -150 |t - 4| + 800$. Calculate.

7. $g(8)$ ____ **200**   **8.** $g(5.5) - g(4.5)$ ____ **-150**

■PROPERTIES   *Objective D*
In 9–12, classify the function as (a) linear, (b) quadratic, or (c) absolute value.

9. $f(x) = 3x^2 + 2x$ ____ **b**   **10.** $y = |\frac{1}{2} x + 5|$ ____ **c**

11. $g(x) = -\frac{2}{3} x + |-7|$ ____ **a**   **12.** $y = |-\frac{2}{3} x| - 7$ ____ **c**

■REPRESENTATIONS   *Objective I*
In 13–16, graph each function.

13. $g(x) = |6 - x|$ **14.** $h(t) = |t| + 4$

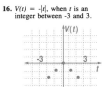

15. $A(r) = |2r|$, when r is between -3 and 3.   **16.** $V(t) = -|t|$, when t is an integer between -3 and 3.

LESSON MASTER 13–4
QUESTIONS ON SPUR OBJECTIVES

■PROPERTIES   *Objective E*   *(See pages 673–675 for objectives.)*

1. What number cannot be in the domain of $f(x) = \dfrac{2}{x - 1}$? ____ **$x = 1$**

In 2–5, give the domain for each function.

2. $f(x) = -7x + 9$ ____ **all reals**

3. $A(t) = t^2 - 4$ ____ **all reals**

4. $g(x) = \sqrt{x}$ ____ **nonneg. reals**

5. $C(n) = 4.5n$, where n is the number of books bought. ____ **nonneg. integers**

In 6–9, give the domain and range.

	Domain	Range
6. $f(x) = 2x + 5$	all reals	all reals
7. $g(x) = |3x + 10|$	all reals	$g(x) \geq 0$
8. $h(t) = \sqrt{t} + 5$	$t \geq 0$	$h(t) \geq 5$
9. $\{(1, 5), (2, 8), (3, 5)\}$	$\{1, 2, 3\}$	$\{5, 8\}$

10. *Multiple choice*   The domain of a function is $\{1, 2, 3\}$. The range is $\{2, 4, 6\}$. Which of these could be the rule for the function?
(a) $y = x + 2$ (b) $y = 2x$ (c) $y = .5x$ (d) $y = 2|x|$ ____ **b, d**

In 11 and 12, give a. the domain and b. the range of each function graphed below.

11. a. domain ____ **{-3, -2, -1, 0, 1}**   **12. a.** domain ____ **$x \geq 0$**

b. range ____ **{0, 1, 2}**   **b.** range ____ **$y \geq 0$**

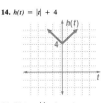

LESSON MASTER 13–5
QUESTIONS ON SPUR OBJECTIVES

■ **USES** *Objective F (See pages 673–675 for objectives.)*
In 1–4, use the spinner to determine the probabilities.

1. P(A) $\frac{1}{3}$

2. P(B) $\frac{1}{6}$

3. P(C) $\frac{1}{6}$

4. P(D) $\frac{1}{3}$

In 5–9, two dice in the shape of a triangular base pyramid are tossed.
The faces are numbered 1 to 4, and are equally likely to appear.

5. P(sum is 2) $\frac{1}{16}$

6. P(sum is 4) $\frac{3}{16}$

7. P(sum is 7) $\frac{1}{8}$

8. P(sum is even) $\frac{1}{2}$

9. The batting average of a baseball player is an indication of the probability
that the player will get a hit in a time at bat. In 1987, Tony Gwynn of San
Diego had a batting average of .369. What was the probability that he
would not get a hit in a time at bat?

$.631$

■ **REPRESENTATIONS** *Objective I*

10. Graph the probability
function for the numbers
on the spinner.

11. Three table tennis balls are
numbered 1, 2, or 3. A ball is
chosen from a box, replaced,
and then another is chosen.
Graph the probability function for
all possible sums.

Algebra © Scott, Foresman and Company   **117**

LESSON MASTER 13–6
QUESTIONS ON SPUR OBJECTIVES

■ **SKILLS** *Objective B (See pages 673–675 for objectives.)*
In 1–6, use a calculator to find each of the values to the nearest
thousandth.

1. tan 22.5° 0.414 2. tan 72.6° 3.191 3. tan 62.7° 1.937

4. tan 7.1° 0.125 5. (tan 60°)² 3.000 6. $\frac{1}{\tan 45°}$ 1.000

In 7–10, find the measure of each angle to the nearest tenth of a degree.

7. m∠A if tan A = 1.036 $46.0°$ 8. m∠B if tan A = .556 $29.1°$

9. m∠C if tan A = .048 $2.7°$ 10. m∠D if tan A = 3.549 $74.3°$

In 11–14, use the picture.

11. tan A = $\frac{5}{12}$ 12. m∠A = $22.6°$

13. tan B = $\frac{12}{5}$ 14. m∠B = $67.4°$

■ **USES** *Objective G*

15. Sara looks up at an angle of 35° to
the top of the Gateway Arch in
St. Louis from a viewing point
900 feet from the base of the Arch.
Approximately how tall is the
Arch if Sara's eyes are 5 feet above
the ground?

about 635 feet

16. Ben's eyes are 170 cm above the
ground. When he stands 20 m
from the base of a fire tower, he
has to look up at an angle of 40° to
see the top. How high is the
tower?

about 18.5 m

17. What angle does the upper half of
the line y = -0.6x + 2 make with
the positive ray of the x-axis?

31°

18. What is the slope of a line which
makes an angle of 68° with the
positive ray of the x-axis?

about 2.48

118   *Algebra © Scott, Foresman and Company*

LESSON MASTER 13–7
QUESTIONS ON SPUR OBJECTIVES

■ **SKILLS** *Objective B (See pages 673–675 for objectives.)*
In 1–14, approximate to the nearest thousandth.

1. $\sqrt{21,443}$ 146.434 2. 11! $39,916,800$

3. $\frac{1}{13}$ 0.077 4. SQR(11.4) 3.376

5. tan 48° 1.111 6. sin 26.5° 0.446

7. log 1000 3 8. cos 143° -0.799

9. $(2.63)^{-2}$ 0.145 10. tan (-25°) -0.466

11. 3! · 4! 144 12. sin 1285° -0.423

13. $\sqrt{0.0256}$ 0.160 14. log 0.789 -0.103

Multiple choice In 15–19, tell which number is not in the domain of the
given function.

15. SQR   (a) 0.5   (b) -4   (c) $(3)^{-2}$ (d) 0 b

16. LOG   (a) 0.5   (b) -4   (c) $\frac{1}{3}$ (d) 1600 b

17. tan   (a) 0.5°   (b) -4°   (c) 1000°   (d) 90° d

18. FACT   (a) 0.5   (b) 2140   (c) 3^2 (d) 0 a

19. $\frac{1}{x}$ (a) 0.5   (b) -4   (c) $(3)^2$ (d) 0 d

Algebra © Scott, Foresman and Company   **119**